The Essential Organizer

An Ongoing Record of Your Estate & Personal Information

William O. Lytle

The Essential Organizer:
An Ongoing Record of Your Estate & Personal Information

By William O. Lytle

Book design by Abdella Design

First printing: August, 2009
Revised edition: 2011

ISBN number: 978-0-615-30088-7

Printed in the United States of America

Comments, suggestions, and questions are welcome.
Please email to: information@essential-organizer.com

To order this book go to: www.essential-organizer.com

Contents

Preface & Introduction

Preparation & Distribution of The Essential Organizer iv
Introduction vi

The Essential Organizer Fast Track

The Express Forms 1

Overview

1 About The Essential Organizer 9
2 How to Use The Essential Organizer 17

Legal & Financial Information

3 Estate Planning Documents 23
4 Insurance Policies 33
5 Financial Assets & Liabilities 41
6 Private Business Ownership 71

Practical Matters

7 Additional Important Documents 81
8 Practical Details of My Everyday Life 95
9 Significant People in My Life 123

Present & Future Health

10 Health Care & Wellness 133
11 Provisions If I Am Unable to Care for Myself 153
12 Arrangements When I Die 161

Family & Friends

13 My Immediate Family 175
14 Family History 193
15 Personal Communications to Family & Friends 197

Appendix & Index

Appendix: Saving & Storing Key Documents 201
Index: Guide to Finding Key Topics 207

Preparation of The Essential Organizer

This book has been prepared by: ______

Address(es): ______

Phone number(s): ______

Email address(es): ______

Date of birth: ______

Social Security number: ______

This book was prepared on (date): ______

It has been updated on (dates): ______

Distribution

Permission is granted to reproduce your completed book for distribution to select individuals.

The following individuals will receive a copy of this book: ______________________

____

____

These additional people should be given a copy if I am unable to care for myself and when I die: ______________________

____

My Signature: ______________________

This book was prepared with the assistance of: ______________________

Signature: ______________________

Introduction

The idea for *The Essential Organizer* began with my neighbor, Faye Rogers Baron, who is a volunteer at a local hospice. She and others frequently witnessed the stress so many family members experienced when, at an already fragile and vulnerable time, they did not know the wishes of their loved ones, either for their personal care or for the management of their estates. These observations, coupled with her experience resolving her own family's complicated estate, led Faye to recognize the need for the development of a comprehensive and user-friendly guidebook for families. This guide would include the basic preferences unique to the life of a loved one as well as the more obvious instructions. As a consequence, Faye suggested that I write this book.

I was showing an early version of the book to my California friends, Gary and Beth, and we were leafing through the section on finances. Beth mentioned that she took care of their checkbook and paid the bills, while her husband handled their investments. Suddenly she looked up and asked, "By the way, Gary, where do you keep those records? And shouldn't our Lucy know where this stuff is even if she is living in New York?" That's when I knew *The Essential Organizer* was on the right track.

Such simple but important questions, when magnified many times over, illustrate what so many people face when a spouse, partner, parent, other family member, or close friend is either incapacitated or dies. With little, if any, preparation they are responsible for carrying out the wishes of their loved one and are confronted with myriad personal and legal issues. All this is on top of their personal distress and the need to ensure the stability of the home. It is vital at this point that they have easy access to essential personal and estate information.

The purpose of *The Essential Organizer* is to provide a place for you to record such information in a form that can be easily understood by the family members, friends, and advisers you designate. It serves as a guide for those who will care for you and your home if you become disabled and when you die. The book covers four categories of information: legal and financial, practical matters, present and future health, and family and friends.

At first glance, this book may seem too long, too detailed, and too demanding, and you may wonder why you should fill it out. There are good reasons to do so. For example, it can: ensure the quality care you want for yourself if you are incapacitated; reassure you that your loved ones and your home will be cared for as you intend; facilitate the settlement of your estate and minimize legal and financial fees; and reduce the time and effort your family must spend later on searching for critical information.

If you take the time to complete *The Essential Organizer* now, you will relieve your loved ones of a significant burden in the future and gain peace of mind as well.

The Essential Organizer Fast Track: The Express Forms

The Purpose of The Express Forms

The Express Forms provide a way for you to quickly prepare essential estate and personal information that is then accessible to family, close friends, and advisers. These forms address a broad range of information related to legal documents, financial assets and liabilities, care of the family and home, your present and future health, and more.

With so many items included in this book, completing all the parts can take considerable time and effort. By highlighting the most essential items, The Express Forms can shorten the time it takes you to prepare critical information.

Before using The Express Forms, please read the "Introduction" on page vi and "About the Essential Organizer" on pages 9-16. These provide information on how to use the book.

Entering Information Into a Table

1. First, read through all the items found on the left side of the Express Form tables on the following pages. Check off those items that are most important to you and your loved ones. Note that next to the heading of the items in each row, there is the page number where these items are covered in more detail in subsequent chapters. Go to these pages if you need to clarify the substance of any item.

2. In the **first column**, for each of the items you select, enter the titles of related documents, statements, certificates, lists, and the like. These both confirm the existence of the item and help to describe it. You may also create a new document where none exists and enter its title in the first column. For example, you might draw up a list of your family and close friends and reference this list. If no documents, statements, and the like exist and you do not wish to create one, you may choose to enter information directly into the table.

3. In the **second column**, enter the physical location of each document, statement, certificate, list, or similar pieces. Specify where each can be found in your home or elsewhere, for example, in a file cabinet, a computer file, a safe deposit box, or your attorney's office.

4. In the **third column**, where applicable, enter the names, addresses, phone/cell/fax numbers, and email addresses of people or organizations who can be contacted for additional information about the specific documents, statements, and the like that you entered in the first column. If you are disabled or die, a family member, your estate executor, or additional individuals you authorize may need to talk with your attorney, accountant, broker, insurance company, and others.

Legal & Financial Information		
For each item: related documents, statements, certificates, lists, and the like	**Physical location of these documents, statements, etc.**	**Contacts for additional information**
Estate Planning Documents (see page 23) ❑ Will ❑ Power of Attorney ❑ Trust agreement ❑ Health care proxy, living will ❑ Divorce/separation, annulment, child custody agreement, adoption		
Insurance Policies (see page 33) ❑ Medical, dental, Medicare Supplemental Insurance (Medigap), disability, long-term care, critical illness ❑ Life ❑ Homeowners, renters, personal liability ❑ Vehicle ❑ Screen names, passwords, PINs, etc. for home computer/online access		

Legal & Financial Information		
For each item: related documents, statements, certificates, lists, and the like	Physical location of these documents, statements, etc	Contacts for additional information
Assets – Sources of Income (see page 41) ❑ Salary/wages, royalties, profit sharing, stock options, pension ❑ Dividends, interest, annuity ❑ Social Security, veterans/government benefits, workers' compensation ❑ Alimony/child support		
Assets – Retirement Accounts (see page 41) ❑ Annuity ❑ IRA, Keogh ❑ 401K, 403B		
Assets – Investments (see page 41) ❑ Stocks, mutual funds, bonds, CDs ❑ U.S. Treasuries, money market funds ❑ Commodities		

Legal & Financial Information		
For each item: related documents, statements, certificates, lists, and the like	**Physical location of these documents, statements, etc**	**Contacts for additional information**
Assets – Other (see page 41) ❑ Primary residence, other homes ❑ Commercial/rental properties ❑ Precious metals, coins, stamps, fine art/antiques		
Liabilities – Loans/Promissory Notes Due (see page 41) ❑ Mortgages, home equity loan ❑ Personal loan, margin loan		
Liabilities – Obligations (see page 41) ❑ Alimony, child support ❑ Credit card debt; property rental, leases; other recurring payments ❑ Promised payments to others ❑ Screen names, passwords, PINs, etc. for home computer/online access		

Practical Matters		
For each item: related documents, statements, certificates, lists, and the like	**Physical location of these documents, statements, etc**	**Contacts for additional information**
Additional Important Documents (see page 81) ❑ Social Security card and statements ❑ Insurance cards: health care, Medicare, Medicare Supplemental Insurance (Medigap) ❑ Marriage, birth, death certificates ❑ Passport, citizenship papers, U.S. visa ❑ Deeds, records of purchase for residences ❑ Titles for vehicles, records of purchase ❑ Tax records, backup files ❑ Current financial records ❑ Professional licenses to practice ❑ Military service papers ❑ Screen names, passwords, PINS, etc. for home computer/online access		

Practical Matters		
For each item: related documents, statements, certificates, lists, and the like	Physical location of these documents, statements, etc	Contacts for additional information
Practical Details of My Everyday Life (see page 95) ❑ Primary residence, contracts, people who have access to my home, cars, P.O. box ❑ Pets ❑ Religious/spiritual affiliation; clergy ❑ Personal service providers: day care, meal preparation, driver, tutor ❑ Home service providers: computers, other electronic equipment, alarm systems, home/yard maintenance, appliance repair, vehicle repair, snowplowing ❑ Utility providers: electricity, gas, oil, water, sewage, phone, TV, Internet ❑ Computer(s) and associated equipment; email address, website ❑ Memberships in organizations ❑ Favorite charities		

Practical Matters		
For each item: related documents, statements, certificates, lists, and the like	**Physical location of these documents, statements, etc**	**Contacts for additional information**
Significant People in My Life (see page 123) ❑ Immediate family, close friends ❑ Family helpers ❑ Clergy ❑ Attorney, accountant, financial planner, assets manager, stockbroker, insurance agents ❑ Business associates, employer, union		
Present & Future Health		
Health Care and Wellness (see page 133) ❑ Primary care providers, specialists, facilities; home care services ❑ Current treatment, medical records ❑ Prescription medications, allergies, pharmacy used ❑ Related insurance ❑ Wellness programs		

Present & Future Health		
For each item: related documents, statements, certificates, lists, and the like	**Physical location of these documents, statements, etc**	**Contacts for additional information**
Provisions if I Am Unable to Care for Myself (see page 153) ❑ People who must be notified immediately, including the person who has my power of attorney ❑ People who will care for my spouse, partner ❑ People who have access to my home ❑ Preferred arrangements if care is necessary ❑ Arrangements for the care of my pets ❑ Instructions for the protection and maintenance of my home		
Arrangements When I Die (see page 161) ❑ People who must be informed immediately ❑ People who will care for my spouse, partner ❑ Funeral arrangements: funeral home, disposition of remains, funeral service preferences ❑ Arrangements for the care of my pets ❑ Instructions for the protection, maintenance, and disposition of my property, possessions		

About The Essential Organizer

When an adult member of a family becomes seriously incapacitated or dies, the spouse, partner, older children, close friends, and key advisers must have rapid access to certain information about that individual's estate and personal life. They need this so they may assume responsibility for this person's welfare, ensure the ongoing stability of family life, and settle inevitable legal issues.

Most of us have prepared a will, established a durable power of attorney, created a trust, drawn up a health care proxy, and executed other standard legal documents. Such estate planning is the cornerstone of providing for our loved ones. When we are no longer able to make critical decisions and when we die, our family and others will need information about these documents. In addition, they must have access to other financial records as well as information about our preferences for care, important relationships, and a variety of practical matters.

Purpose

The Essential Organizer provides a place for you to record estate and personal information that is then accessible to designated family, friends, and advisers, such as your attorney and estate executor. It will help you identify information vital to these individuals, especially in a crisis, and it will serve as a place to document the nature and location of this information. When completed and maintained, *The Essential Organizer* will become an ongoing record of the information you wish to make available as guidance for those who must act on your behalf should you become disabled by an illness or accident and when you die. You will have the opportunity to record an array of data in this book related to four categories of information: legal and financial, practical matters,

Legal & Financial

Practical Matters

Present & Future Health

Family & Friends

1 About The Essential Organizer

Notes

health—present and future, and family and friends. It makes sense to prepare and share this information while you still enjoy good physical and mental health.

Confidentiality

One objective of *The Essential Organizer* is to ensure a significant level of privacy for your personal information. To this end, it is best not to include in this book confidential information such as details of specific investments, beneficiaries of insurance policies, or the nature of your medical treatments. In place of this, you are asked to record the titles of documents that contain this sensitive information, where they can be found, and whom to contact for clarification and additional information. Filling in this kind of information reduces the chances that someone could gain information that would unduly benefit them. Therefore, your decision on what to put in the book depends in part on the level of confidentiality you wish to maintain.

Benefits

The Essential Organizer can benefit you and others in a variety of ways. It can:

- Provide a check on the thoroughness of your estate planning and help you tie up any loose ends
- Serve as a way to start important family conversations about your estate planning and other family matters, discussions that can help reassure your family and reduce misunderstandings and disagreement
- Reassure you that your loved ones will be taken care of in the manner you intend
- Help ensure that if you are incapacitated, your treatment will be in accordance with your wishes
- Provide guidance for maintaining the family home if you are seriously ill and when you die
- Reduce the time and effort your family must expend during a stressful period

searching for essential information, especially critical documents such as your will, insurance policies, records of assets, and the names of key individuals such as your estate executor and the trustees of your trusts
- Facilitate the settlement of your estate and minimize legal and financial fees

Many individuals, with or without families, feel very close to trusted friends and depend on them for support. The pairing of "close friends" with "family" throughout the book indicates that both groups may need the information recorded here.

Contents

The Essential Organizer is divided into seven parts which contain the chapters shown below along with examples of the topics addressed in each.

The Essential Organizer Fast Track
The Express Forms
Overview
1. **About *The Essential Organizer*:** purpose and benefits, contents, recording information, getting started, distribution
2. **How to Use *The Essential Organizer:*** filling out worksheets, what to record and not record, options for entering information

Legal & Financial Information

3. **Estate Planning Documents:** will, durable power of attorney, health care proxy, living will, divorce, and child custody agreements
4. **Insurance Policies:** medical, Medicare Supplemental Insurance (Medigap), disability, long-term care, life, homeowners, liability, vehicle
5. **Financial Assets & Liabilities:** sources of income, retirement accounts, investments; loans and other debts

***The Essential Organizer* can benefit you and others in a variety of ways. It can:**

- Provide a check on your estate planning and help you tie up any loose ends
- Serve as a way to start important family conversations
- Reassure you that your loved ones will be taken care of in the manner you intend
- Help ensure that if you are incapacitated, your treatment will be in accordance with your wishes
- Provide guidance for maintaining the family home if you are seriously ill and when you die
- Reduce the time and effort your family must expend during a stressful period searching for essential information
- Facilitate the settlement of your estate and minimize legal and financial fees

1 About The Essential Organizer

Other Resources

You can find additional information about estate planning and documentation in libraries, bookstores, and on the Web. Try searching online with Google™ and Yahoo!® using such terms as estate planning, legal definitions, financial records, advance medical directives, and the like.

Four excellent sources are:

- **AARP℠:** www.aarp.org/money/financial_planning, or 1-888-687-2277
- **American Bar Association – Guide to Wills and Estates:** www.abanet.org/publiced/practical/books/wills/home.html, or 1-312-988-5735
- **Internal Revenue Service:** www.irs.gov/taxtopics/tc451.html, or 1-800-829-4933
- **Nolo®:** www.nolo.com, or 1-800-728-3555; this company offers readable books, articles, forms, and software on a wide range of legal subjects.

6. **Private Business Ownership:** name, type, partners and percentage interest of ownership, assets, liabilities

Practical Matters

7. **Additional Important Documents:** Social Security and Medicare cards, birth certificates, deeds, military service records
8. **Practical Details of My Everyday Life:** residences, pets, religious/spiritual affiliation, service providers, memberships
9. **Significant People in My Life:** family members, friends, caregivers, clergy, attorney, physician, work colleagues

Present & Future Health

10. **Health Care & Wellness:** providers of medical care, home care services used, medications, wellness activities
11. **Provisions if I Am Unable to Care for Myself:** people to notify, preferred arrangements, care of pets and home
12. **Arrangements When I Die:** people to inform, funeral home, cemetery, burial or cremation, funeral service preferences, care of pets and home

Family & Friends

13. **My Immediate Family:** names and information about family members—spouse, partner, children, parents, siblings
14. **Family History:** related information—genealogy records, stories, photographs, letters, artifacts, recordings
15. **Personal Communications to Family & Friends:** plans for communicating your private thoughts, feelings, beliefs

Appendix

Saving & Storing Key Documents: what documents to save, for how long, and where to store them

Guide to Finding Key Topics: index of the major topics covered in the book

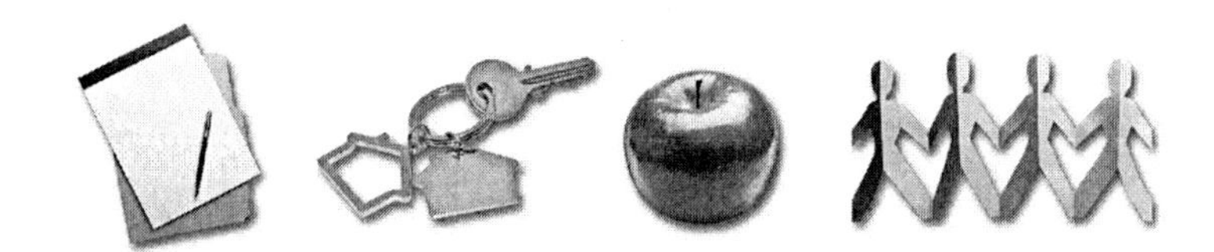

Recording Essential Information

Each of the tables in the chapters that follow contains items or topics on the left side of the table, for example, types of insurance, financial investments, and service providers. For those items that are important to you, you'll enter the titles of existing documents, statements, certificates, lists, and the like. In addition, you'll record their current physical location and the people to contact for more particulars if needed. If such documents do not exist, you may choose to create and reference new ones, or you may enter the needed information directly into this book.

For *The Essential Organizer* to meet your specific needs you will decide what information you want to record and the level of detail required. The introduction to each chapter lists the items addressed so you can identify those that are important to you and those that are not. When choosing the information to document, consider these criteria:

- Relevance/usefulness of the information to your family, friends, and advisers
- Consequences if certain information is not collected and shared
- Ease of collecting the information
- Your willingness to disclose this information to others

Ask your spouse, partner, grown children, and others what they want to know more about and what information will be important to them when you are no longer around. This will help you decide which items to include and which to disregard. It's possible that they will identify issues you have not considered.

Completeness and Accessibility of Information

Filling out *The Essential Organizer* will help you check on the existence, completeness, and location of various documents. You may find they are in good shape or discover you have more work to do. It's important to organize and store your records so your family will find them readily accessible and easy to understand. If these are now in a number of different places in your home, consider consolidating them in a single

Notes

Notes

location. (For information on how long various documents should be saved and where they should be stored, see the Appendix: "Saving & Storing Key Documents" on page 201.)

Getting Started

With so many items included in *The Essential Organizer*, you may wonder where you should begin. If you need to provide information to your loved ones quickly, then go to the chapter, The Express Forms, on page 1 and use the forms provided there. This will help you ensure that the truly critical information is made available to key individuals in a short time.

If time is not an immediate issue, fill out Chapters 3, 4, 5, 7, 10, 11, 12; these deal with estate planning documents, insurance policies, financial assets and liabilities, other important documents, health care and wellness, provisions if you are unable to care for yourself, and arrangements when you die. When these are completed, you will have filled out the chapters that contain information that is most essential to your family and others, especially in difficult times. Then address those remaining chapters that are of the greatest interest or importance to you.

If you feel a bit overwhelmed as you look though the book, remember that there is no single best way to use this book. You will complete only those parts you find useful; it's very unlikely that every item in each chapter will apply to you. Also, you can fill in the information over a period of time at a pace that suits you. In addition, notice that the book's size is due in large part to the amount of space provided for recording data. Furthermore, you may already have pulled together much of this information. If you are finding it difficult to focus your efforts, consider asking a few family members and friends to sit down together to help you identify the items of greatest importance.

You and your spouse or partner will want to fill out separate books; even though there may be considerable overlap, much of the content will be unique to each of you. However, you can support one another by filling out your respective books together.

If you find that you are unable to fill out *The Essential Organizer* for whatever reason, then consider simply using the book as a guide for talking about important items with key individuals.

It may help to remember that the time it takes you to complete this task will be a fraction of the time your family will have to spend later on if this work is not done. Once you have completed *The Essential Organizer*, you can rest assured that you have removed a significant burden from your loved ones. Addressing these issues now will bring you peace of mind in the future.

Distributing *The Essential Organizer*

You'll probably want to share your completed book with your spouse, partner, older children, certain other family members, close friends, the executor of your estate, and key advisers. Be sure to include those who will have an obligation to manage your affairs in the future should you be unable to do so. While you'll want to give the book to a limited number of people when it's first completed, you may designate that it be distributed to others should you become seriously ill and when you die. You also may choose to give only certain parts to specific individuals; for example, you may give the instructions for your funeral to your clergy and to the director of your preferred funeral home. You have permission to reproduce and distribute your completed book or specific sections to others.

Be careful about what you enter into this book and whom you choose to receive it. Also be sure to store it in a safe place in your home.

When you have completed *The Essential Organizer*, consider getting together with select family and friends to talk about the contents. This discussion can provide you the opportunity to explain your entries in the book, and it could lead to a conversation about your estate planning, your wishes and expectations, and other personal issues if you so choose. This also may help minimize misunderstandings that could otherwise

Disclaimer

This book, *The Essential Organizer: An Ongoing Record of Your Estate & Personal Information*, in no way replaces the need for professional legal, accounting, financial, or medical advice. You should contact your attorney, accountant, financial adviser, or health care provider for appropriate counsel. Be aware that some of the documents discussed in *The Essential Organizer* are regulated by laws that may vary from state to state.

Also, *The Essential Organizer* does not attempt to list or describe all the types of trusts, insurance policies, retirement plans, and the like that are available. Other sources, both in print and online, can provide this information. Remember that the purpose of *The Essential Organizer* is not to prescribe but to document the choices you have already made.

Note: a number of the legal and financial documents and plans that are listed in this book are specific to the United States. That said, with appropriate adaptation *The Essential Organizer* may be useful to people in other countries.

Notes

develop among your loved ones after you're gone. Remember that you need not discuss all the details of your planning, for example, the provisions of your will. Also, bear in mind that it will probably be easier for you to initiate this discussion than for your children to do so.

Updating *The Essential Organizer*

Change occurs rapidly these days and records can become outdated in no time. Obsolescence can be caused, for example, by changes in your marital status, children, job, residence, health, financial condition, the state where you live, or state and federal laws. Ideally, you should update your book when any significant change occurs, especially with critical items such as estate planning documents, insurance policies, assets and liabilities, and your health. Remember, also, that items that do not apply to you today may become relevant some time in the future. At the very least, think about setting aside a time each year to check on the accuracy and completeness of your records. Record the dates of your revisions on page iv. You may want to send these changes to those individuals who have already received your book.

How to Use The Essential Organizer

In *The Essential Organizer* you will record a broad range of critical information related to the existence of estate planning documents, financial assets and liabilities, provisions if you are disabled, and the like. In each chapter you will find worksheets that contain either three-column tables or other spaces to be filled in. In chapters with tables, a sample table is provided in the introduction.

Here are some guidelines for entering information into a table. (See the sample tables on pages 19-21.)

First read through all the items listed on the left side of each table in each chapter. Check off those items that are important to you and your loved ones. Note that the title in the gray bar at the top of each table is the subject for the items on that page. Then, for each item, enter the information you think is important.

In the **first column** of a table, you can choose one of three ways to present the requested information. These options are clarified in chapter introductions.

1. You can enter the titles of documents, statements, certificates, lists, and the like which describe and confirm the existence of your insurance policies, investments, and such. See the sample table for "Estate Planning Documents" on page 19.
2. You can create a new document where none exists and enter its title in the first column. For example, you could draw up a list of your close friends and reference this list. See the sample table for "Significant People" on page 20. You may compose such a list on a computer, or you can type it or write it by hand if you prefer.
3. If no documents, statements, certificates, lists, or the like exist and you do not want to create new ones, you can enter information directly into this book. For example, you might enter the names and locations of specific family photos and heirlooms. See the sample table for "Family History" on page 21.

Notes

2 How to Use The Essential Organizer

Entering Data

These instructions are intended as a guide for recording information in the tables. Certainly you should enter any information that you think will be helpful to your family, friends, and advisers.

If you are going to write in this book, use a pencil or erasable ink as this will make it easier to revise entries in the future.

The CD included with the book enables you to use your computer to enter information in the spaces provided. This also makes it relatively easy to change your entries, store the information securely on your hard drive, and send copies of your information to family, friends, and advisers. It also ensures the legibility of your entries.

In the **second column**, enter the physical location of each document, statement, certificate, list, or similar item. Specify where each can be found in your home or elsewhere; for example, in a file cabinet, a computer file, a safe deposit box, or your attorney's office. See the sample tables.

In the **third column**, where applicable, insert the names, addresses, phone/cell/fax numbers, and email addresses of people or organizations who can be contacted for additional information about the specific documents, statements, certificates, lists, and the like that you entered in the first column. If you are disabled or die, a family member, the estate executor, or other individuals you authorize may need to talk with your attorney, accountant, insurance agent, and others. See the sample tables.

You will find some duplication of items within the book, for example, types of investments and names of health care providers. In some cases you may choose to record the necessary detail in a single location with no need to repeat it. In other cases you may want to duplicate this information for ease of reference.

If you make no entries in a particular chapter, note this on its first page so that a family member or friend will not waste time searching for information that is not there.

It's becoming increasingly common for people to store information on computer-related sites. These may be in files on their computer hard drive, on an external hard drive, on CDs that are kept in the home or in a safe deposit box, or in online websites that offer storage space for a fee. If any of this is true for you, be sure to reference these physical locations in the second column. Also state where your confidential user names, passwords, and PINs—those that allow access to your files—may be found.

Sample Table This is a copy of the table on page 28 in Chapter 3.

Property & Financial Documents		
For each item: related documents, statements, certificates, lists, and the like	Physical location of these documents, statements, etc.	Contacts for additional information
☑ Will (including codicils) I have a will. Executor(s) of my estate: My wife and attorney Document last updated: 2/1/06	The original is in my attorney's safe; a copy is in my file cabinet at home.	Attorney: H.I. Jones 123 Any Street City, State 12345 555-121-1212 hijones@- - - -.com
☑ Durable power of attorney Attorney-in-fact: My wife has power of attorney. Document last updated: 6/7/98	Same as above	Same as above
☑ Trust agreement My wife and I have a trust agreement. Trustees of the trust: My wife and I Document last updated: 6/15/05	Same as above	Same as above

2 How to Use The Essential Organizer

Sample Table This is a copy of the table on page 125 in Chapter 9.

Family & Friends		
For each item: related documents, statements, certificates, lists, and the like	Physical location of these documents, statements, etc.	Contacts for additional information
☑ Immediate family members Immediate family members are listed.	See Chapter 13 in this book, "My Immediate Family," for names and contact information for family members.	My husband will have additional information if needed.
☑ Extended family members These names are in my address book in my desk.	My desk drawer.	My husband will have additional information if needed.
☑ Close friends I have prepared a list of my close friends and their contact information.	This list is in a folder in my computer called "Close Friends," which is in my hard drive's "Documents" folder. Also printed and stored in my file cabinet at home.	My husband will have additional information if needed.

Sample Table This is a copy of the table on page 194 in Chapter 14.

Family History: Documents & Recordings		
For each item: related documents, statements, certificates, lists, and the like	Physical location of these documents, statements, etc.	Contacts for additional information
☑ **Family documents, photographs, artifacts** A genealogy of my family has been written and distributed by my niece, Rachel LeBlanc. I also have old family photos and a scrapbook belonging to my great-grandmother. I have drawn up a list of the family antiques in my home, including quilts, a clock, a wash-stand, sleigh bells, and a table .	My copy is contained in a folder called, "Family History," in my file cabinet at home. A list of these items is in the above folder.	Rachel LeBlanc 123 Any Street City, State 12345 555-121-1212 rlb@- - - -.com Contact my wife.
☑ **Family recordings: movies, videotapes/DVDs, audiotapes/CDs** Rachel also has started holding video interviews with senior family members. I have transferred to a DVD a number of old home movies dating back to the 1930s. My children and grandchildren have a copy.	Rachel has these. See above	Contact Rachel. Contact my wife or my children.

Notes

Estate Planning Documents

This chapter provides the place to record information about your legal estate planning documents, such as a will, a durable power of attorney, and a health care proxy. Many of these documents ensure that your wishes will be carried out if you are incapacitated and unable to make important decisions as well as when you die. For example, some documents specify how your financial assets are to be distributed and used in the future; others include instructions for the welfare of your children, other family members, and friends; and some deal with your preferred treatment if you are seriously ill or disabled.

In addition to the standard documents, there are several others listed on the next page that are linked with estate planning and directly affect its contents. These include legal agreements associated with marriage, its dissolution, and related children. Also listed are estate financial analyses and plans; while not legal documents, these are included because they produce information that underpins much estate planning.

The **first column** in the following tables lists the names of the traditional estate planning documents and associated documents. (See the sample table on page 28.) Check off each of the items that is pertinent to you. Then for each, enter in this column the title and other identifying information for related documents, statements, certificates, lists, and the like. Where required, include the date when the document was created or last updated. You will want to review these documents from time to time to be sure they are still accurate, up to date, and reflect your intentions. If the laws governing these have changed, your attorney should advise you of their significance. If you see the name of any document on this list that you do not recognize, contact your attorney to find out if you should have it.

In the **second column**, enter the physical location of each document, both the signed originals and the copies.

Definitions Directory

Property and Financial Documents 25
- Will
- Durable power of attorney
- Trust agreement
- Private foundation
- Declaration of homestead

Medical Documents (Advance Medical Directives) 26
- Health care proxy
- Living will

3 Estate Planning Documents

Notes

In the **third column** enter the name of the person(s) or organization(s) to contact for additional information, such as your attorney or the law firm; include contact information such as addresses, phone numbers, and email addresses.

The following are the estate planning and associated documents covered in this chapter. While not all will be relevant to you, there is a good chance you will have a number of these. Definitions are found on pages 25-27.

Property and Financial Documents 29

- Will
- Durable power of attorney
- Trust agreement
- Private foundation
- Declaration of homestead

Medical Documents (Advance Medical Directives) 30

- Health care proxy
- Living will

"Care of Others" Documents 31

- Special financial and personal care arrangements for disabled or aged individuals
- Appointment of the guardian and the property trustee for minor or special needs children; letters of requests and instructions

Associated Documents 32

- Prenuptial agreement
- Divorce, legal separation, annulment, property settlement, and child custody agreements; adoption papers
- Pending legal issues
- Estate financial analyses and plans

Definitions of Common Estate Planning Documents

Will

A will is a document that specifies how your property is to be distributed or transferred upon your death, that is, which assets go to whom and when. A will may be simple or complex depending on the nature of your estate. When you die, your estate executor(s) is responsible for settling your estate according to your instructions and ensuring that your will is probated through the appropriate court. You may make changes to a will, known as codicils, which can contain additions and amendments without redoing the entire document. Also, you may write a "personal property memorandum" in which you list and dispose of items of tangible personal property not specifically covered in your will. This document must be referenced in the will, but it is not a codicil and cannot alter the will. The memorandum itself may be changed at any time.

Durable Power of Attorney

In a durable power of attorney you authorize a person(s) to act on your behalf when you are incapacitated; this individual(s) is called your "attorney-in-fact." As your agent, this person usually deals with financial matters and, for example, may access your bank accounts, sign your name on checks, and make decisions about your retirement accounts, including buying and selling securities. The document is in force upon signing and is valid until its revocation or the death of the grantor.

Trust Agreement

A trust is a legal mechanism by which you can place your property in a "trust" to be managed by a trustee(s), who you appoint to carry out your instructions for the benefit of designated beneficiaries, which can include yourself. A trust agreement sets up the terms of the trust, including the property it encompasses, the beneficiaries, and

Notes

Notes

the conditions for distribution. The trust continues for your lifetime even if you are incapacitated and may continue after your death. The majority of trusts are revocable, which allows you to modify or close them. Trusts help minimize the expense, time, and publicity of probate. There are many different kinds of trusts that can be established for various purposes.

Private Foundation

A private foundation is a nonprofit organization established and funded by an individual, a family, or a group to accomplish specified charitable goals. The principal or endowment is invested and the income is paid out annually to the charity. The foundation is required to distribute annual grants totaling a minimum of 5% of the value of the assets. It is exempt from federal income tax on its income, avoids capital gains tax, and minimizes estate tax liability. The founder and family members can be appointed trustees of the foundation and may be paid for work performed for the benefit of the foundation. Several types of private foundations exist.

Declaration of Homestead

This document provides protection for your principal residence against seizure or attachment by unsecured creditors at a time when you are experiencing financial difficulties. The amount of exemption allowed is set by the state. Recognition of such a declaration and its terms may vary from state to state.

Health Care Proxy

In your health care proxy, the first part of your advance medical directives, you appoint a trusted individual(s) to act as your advocate or agent to make health care decisions on your behalf in the event you are incapable of doing so. This person may be called a health care advocate, agent, surrogate, or personal representative.

A proxy does not spell out the substance of the decisions that may be made; it simply names the person who is authorized to make them. Having a proxy is especially critical should a decision be necessary regarding the removal of life support. This person also may make a decision as to the disposition of your remains immediately after your death. The legal powers that an advocate or agent can assume may vary from state to state.

Every health care proxy must comply with the Privacy Rule of the Health Insurance Portability and Accountability Act (HIPAA). This is a federal law that protects a person's health care privacy and limits the disclosure of protected information by a health care provider. It is essential that your proxy contain a HIPAA waiver or release so that a medical provider will be able to provide pertinent medical information to the person you have named as your advocate or agent.

Living Will

This document is the second part of your advance medical directives. The health care proxy above names the person(s) who is authorized to make health care decisions for you. The living will states your instructions in writing as to your treatment when you're dying and are unable to speak for yourself. It provides clarity about your wishes to your family, your physician, and others. This document deals with the medical treatment you want or don't want to receive during a terminal illness, including what life-prolonging procedures you want continued or removed. This may also include your wish to donate your organs for transplanting or research. A living will takes effect only when you are so incapacitated that you can no longer communicate your instructions yourself. Check to be sure your living will meets the requirements of the state in which you reside.

Notes

3 Estate Planning Documents

Sample Table

Property & Financial Documents		
For each item: related documents, statements, certificates, lists, and the like	**Physical location of these documents, statements, etc.**	**Contacts for additional information**
☑ **Will (including codicils)** I have a will. **Executor(s) of my estate:** My wife and attorney **Document last updated:** 2/1/06	The original is in my attorney's safe; a copy is in my file cabinet at home.	Attorney: H.I. Jones 123 Any Street City, State 12345 555-121-1212 hijones@- - - -.com
☑ **Durable power of attorney** **Attorney-in-fact:** My wife has power of attorney. **Document last updated:** 6/7/98	Same as above	Same as above
☑ **Trust agreement** My wife and I have a trust agreement. **Trustees of the trust:** My wife and I **Document last updated:** 6/15/05	Same as above	Same as above

Property & Financial Documents		
For each item: related documents, statements, certificates, lists, and the like	Physical location of these documents, statements, etc.	Contacts for additional information
❑ Will (including codicils) Executor(s) of my estate: Document last updated:		
❑ Durable power of attorney Attorney-in-fact: Document last updated:		
❑ Trust agreement Trustee(s) of the trust: Document last updated:		

3 Estate Planning Documents

Property & Financial Documents		
For each item: related documents, statements, certificates, lists, and the like	Physical location of these documents, statements, etc.	Contacts for additional information
❑ Private foundation Document last updated:		
❑ Declaration of homestead Document last updated:		

Medical Documents (Advance Medical Directives)		
For each item: related documents, statements, certificates, lists, and the like	Physical location of these documents, statements, etc.	Contacts for additional information
❑ Health care proxy Document last updated:		
❑ Living will Document last updated:		

"Care of Others" Documents		
For each item: related documents, statements, certificates, lists, and the like	Physical location of these documents, statements, etc.	Contacts for additional information
❑ Special financial and personal care arrangements for disabled or aged individuals		
❑ Appointment of the guardian and the property trustee for minor or special needs children; letters of requests and instructions		

3 Estate Planning Documents

Associated Documents		
For each item: related documents, statements, certificates, lists, and the like	Physical location of these documents, statements, etc.	Contacts for additional information
❑ Prenuptial agreement		
❑ Divorce, legal separation, annulment, property settlement, and child custody agreements; adoption papers		
❑ Pending legal issues		
❑ Estate financial analyses and plans		

Insurance Policies

In this chapter you will record information about your insurance policies, both those you own and those that are provided by others. The **first column** of the following tables contains the names of common types of insurance. (See the sample table on page 34.) Check off each type of policy you carry; then record the title of any documents, statements, certificates, and lists related to your insurance policies; include the name of the insurance company and policy numbers or other identifying information. Note that policies may be paid for by you personally, by your employer or union, or by a government organization.

In the **second column**, enter the physical location of the documents, including beneficiary forms where applicable. In the **third column**, enter the name of the person and the organization that can be contacted for additional information about the policies; this probably will be your insurance agent, someone at the insurance company, or an administrator at your employer, union, or other organization. Include their addresses, phone numbers, and email addresses.

You probably will not want to include the value of your policies or the beneficiaries in these tables.

This chapter covers the types of insurance policies, shown in the sidebar to the right. You may want to use this list to evaluate the sufficiency of the insurance you now carry.

Medical and Life Insurance 35
- Medical insurance
- Dental insurance
- Medicare Supplemental Insurance (Medigap)
- Disability insurance
- Long-term care insurance
- Critical illness insurance
- Life insurance
- Travel and accidental death insurance

Property Insurance 37
- Homeowner's/property, flood, and earthquake insurance; riders
- Renter's insurance
- Mortgage and title insurance
- Personal liability insurance
- Vehicle insurance
- Watercraft insurance
- Aircraft insurance

Other Insurance 39
- Other types of policies
- Insurance you own that covers others
- Insurance owned by others that covers you

4 Insurance Policies

Sample Table

Medical & Life Insurance		
For each item: related documents, statements, certificates, lists, and the like	**Physical location of these documents, statements, etc.**	**Contacts for additional information**
☑ **Medical insurance** I have the Commonwealth Health Plan. ID# 0123456	This policy is in my file cabinet at home.	Commonwealth Health Plan 123 Any Street City, State 12345 555-121-1212
☑ **Dental insurance** I don't have dental insurance.		
☑ **Medicare Supplemental Insurance (Medigap)** See medical insurance above.	See above	See above
☑ **Disability insurance** I discontinued my disability insurance when I retired.		

Medical & Life Insurance		
For each item: related documents, statements, certificates, lists, and the like	Physical location of these documents, statements, etc.	Contacts for additional information
❑ Medical insurance		
❑ Dental insurance		
❑ Medicare Supplemental Insurance (Medigap)		
❑ Disability insurance		

4 Insurance Policies

Medical & Life Insurance		
For each item: related documents, statements, certificates, lists, and the like	Physical location of these documents, statements, etc.	Contacts for additional information
❑ Long-term care insurance		
❑ Critical illness insurance		
❑ Life insurance		
❑ Travel and accidental death insurance		

Property Insurance		
For each item: related documents, statements, certificates, lists, and the like	Physical location of these documents, statements, etc.	Contacts for additional information
❑ Homeowner's/property, flood, and earthquake insurance; riders to cover special items such as antiques, fine art, or computer equipment		
❑ Renter's insurance		
❑ Mortgage and title insurance		
❑ Personal liability – umbrella insurance		

4 Insurance Policies

Property Insurance		
For each item: related documents, statements, certificates, lists, and the like	Physical location of these documents, statements, etc.	Contacts for additional information
❑ Vehicle insurance: auto, recreational (RV), off-road (ATV), snowmobile, motorcycle, truck, farm/heavy equipment		
❑ Watercraft insurance		
❑ Aircraft insurance		

Other Insurance		
For each item: related documents, statements, certificates, lists, and the like	Physical location of these documents, statements, etc.	Contacts for additional information
❑ Other types of policies		
❑ Insurance you own that covers others		
❑ Insurance owned by others that covers you		
❑ Access to accounts, documents, files on home computer/websites; account names and numbers, PINs, screen names, user names, passwords		

4 Insurance Policies

Notes

Financial Assets & Liabilities

In this chapter you will record information about your financial assets and liabilities, some of the most important data you'll provide to family, friends, and advisers. The types of assets and liabilities addressed are listed on the next two pages. Take special care to list all assets; if the executor of your estate cannot locate or identify certain assets when you die, they cannot be distributed to the intended beneficiaries.

Remember that this book is not the place to list the confidential details of your assets and liabilities, such as specific retirement accounts you own and their value. Rather, you are asked to record the titles of statements or documents that confirm their existence, where these are located, and who may be contacted for additional information.

In the **first column** of the following tables, check off each type of asset or liability you hold, such as an IRA account or a home equity loan. (See the sample table on page 45.) Then enter the title of the document or statement that verifies your ownership plus identification data such as a certificate number. Include the name of any related organizations such as: current or past employer; financial institution like a brokerage house, asset management company, retirement plan administrator, bank, or credit union; or the U.S. or state government. As an option, you may create and reference a list of certain items, for example, antiques or fine art you own. Some information you may choose to enter directly in the appropriate space.

In the **second column**, record the physical location of this information, such as your file cabinet or computer files. In the **third column**, list the names of individuals and organizations who can provide additional information: for example, a broker, loan officer, attorney, financial planner, or pension plan administrator and their associated companies; include addresses, phone numbers, and email addresses. If you have questions about your assets, contact these individuals.

Notes

5 Financial Assets & Liabilities

Notes

Identify any asset that is held jointly or contains a payable-on-death or transfer-on-death provision. Although you will not want to list account names or numbers, computer screen names, user names, passwords, or PINs in these tables, do state where those can be found.

Note that there is duplication of some items listed under both "Sources of Income" and "Investments," for example, Stocks, Bonds, U.S. Treasuries, and Certificates of Deposit. Record necessary details in whichever location you prefer; there is no need to repeat this information.

Types of Financial Assets & Liabilities

Financial Assets

Sources of Income 46

- Salary/wages
- Pension
- Social Security; SSI
- Veterans/government benefits
- Workers' compensation
- Profit sharing
- Deferred compensation
- Stock options
- Royalties
- Annuity
- Alimony/child support
- Distribution from trusts; gifts
- Dividends: stocks; mutual funds; partnerships
- Interest
  - U.S. Treasuries
  - Bonds: U.S., state, municipal, corporate
  - Certificates of Deposit
  - Money market funds
  - Personal loans made to others
  - Bank, credit union accounts; safe deposit box

Retirement Accounts.......................... 54

- Annuity
- IRA
- SIMPLE IRA
- Roth IRA
- SEP-IRA
- Keogh
- 401K
- 403B

Investments 57
- Stocks
- Mutual funds
- Partnerships
- U.S. Treasuries
- Bonds: U.S., state, municipal, corporate
- Certificates of Deposit
- Money market funds
- Commodities
- Negotiable certificates
- Foreign: currency, property

Real Estate/Properties 60
- Primary residence
- Other homes, timeshares
- Commercial/rental properties

Tangible Assets 61
- Vehicles; watercraft; aircraft
- Precious metals
- Jewelry
- Coins; stamps
- Antiques; fine art
- Valuable collections

Other Assets 64
- Insurance policies with cash value
- Anticipated inheritance and/or gifts
- Lines of credit
- Credit, debit, travel cards
- Uncollected legal judgments, claims, pending lawsuits in my favor

Financial Liabilities

Loans/Promissory Notes Due 67
- Mortgages; reverse mortgages
- Home equity loans
- Vehicles, watercraft, aircraft loan/lease
- Personal loans; family loans
- Margin loans

Obligations 69
- Alimony/child support
- Credit card debt
- Property rental/lease
- Automatic deductions from bank accounts
- Promised contributions to organizations
- Agreements to provide financial support or care for others
- Unpaid legal judgments, claims, pending lawsuits not in my favor; consequences of identity theft; additional money owed
- Access to accounts: computer/website

Notes

5 Financial Assets & Liabilities

Notes

Definitions of Tax-advantaged Retirement Plans

Several types of tax-advantaged retirement plans are listed in this chapter. These differ in the qualifications for individuals who may be included in a plan; the limits on the amount of money that can be placed in a plan and the timing; the amounts that must be withdrawn and the timing; and the amount of taxes that must be paid and when. Here are brief definitions of these plans:

- **IRA** (Individual Retirement Account): a personal savings plan that permits a person to set aside money for retirement; contributions and accrued earnings are not subject to income tax until they are distributed
- **SIMPLE IRA** (Savings Incentive Match Plan for Employees): an employer-provided plan funded by a pretax salary reduction; tax deferred until money is distributed; simpler and less costly administration—ideal for small employers
- **Roth IRA**: similar to a traditional IRA except that contributions to the plan are subject to income tax before they are placed in the plan; then the distributions are tax-free
- **SEP-IRA** (Simplified Employee Pension): a plan in which employers may make contributions toward their employees' retirement and, if self-employed, toward their own retirement
- **Keogh**: a retirement plan for self-employed professionals or sole proprietors and their employees; the amount in the account grows tax free until withdrawn
- **401K**: a deferred compensation plan in which an employer can contribute a portion of an employee's cash wages to the plan on a pre-tax basis; deferred wages and earnings accrue tax free; taxes are paid when these are distributed
- **403B**: a retirement plan for certain employees of public schools and tax-exempt organizations

Sample Table

Financial Assets: Sources of Income		
For each item: related documents, statements, certificates, lists, and the like	**Physical location of these documents, statements, etc.**	**Contacts for additional information**
☑ **Salary/wages; automatic deposit to bank account** I have income from my consulting clients.	Invoices, check stubs, and 1099s are in my file cabinet at home.	My accountant has information about past years' income. J.P. Goldman 123 Any Street City, State 12345 555-121-1212
☑ **Pension (including survivor benefits); automatic deposit to bank account** I receive a pension from prior employment at DEF Corp.; automatic deposit to my bank account.	Bank statements are in my file cabinet at home.	Central Bank 123 Any Street City, State 12345 555-121-1212
☑ **Social Security; Supplemental Security Insurance survivor benefit; automatic deposit to bank account** Monthly payments are automatically deposited to my bank account.	Statements are in my file cabinet at home.	Same as above

5 Financial Assets & Liabilities

Financial Assets: Sources of Income		
For each item: related documents, statements, certificates, lists, and the like	Physical location of these documents, statements, etc.	Contacts for additional information
❑ Salary/wages; automatic deposit to bank account		
❑ Pension (including survivor benefits); automatic deposit to bank account		
❑ Social Security; Supplemental Security Insurance survivor benefit; automatic deposit to bank account		

Financial Assets: Sources of Income		
For each item: related documents, statements, certificates, lists, and the like	Physical location of these documents, statements, etc.	Contacts for additional information
❑ Veterans/government benefits; automatic deposit to bank account		
❑ Workers' compensation		
❑ Profit sharing		
❑ Deferred compensation		

5 Financial Assets & Liabilities

Financial Assets: Sources of Income		
For each item: related documents, statements, certificates, lists, and the like	Physical location of these documents, statements, etc.	Contacts for additional information
❑ Stock options		
❑ Royalties		
❑ Annuity		
❑ Alimony/child support		
❑ Distribution from trusts; gifts		

Financial Assets: Sources of Income–Dividends		
For each item: related documents, statements, certificates, lists, and the like	Physical location of these documents, statements, etc.	Contacts for additional information
❑ Stocks		
❑ Mutual funds		
❑ Partnerships		

5 Financial Assets & Liabilities

Financial Assets: Sources of Income–Interest		
For each item: related documents, statements, certificates, lists, and the like	Physical location of these documents, statements, etc.	Contacts for additional information
❑ U.S. Treasuries		
❑ U.S. bonds		
❑ State, municipal bonds		
❑ Corporate bonds		

Financial Assets: Sources of Income–Interest		
For each item: related documents, statements, certificates, lists, and the like	Physical location of these documents, statements, etc.	Contacts for additional information
❑ Certificates of Deposit (CDs)		
❑ Money market funds		
❑ Personal loans made to family members (including arrangements)		
❑ Personal loans made to other individuals		

5 Financial Assets & Liabilities

Financial Assets: Sources of Income–Interest		
For each item: related documents, statements, certificates, lists, and the like	Physical location of these documents, statements, etc.	Contacts for additional information
❑ Bank/credit union name(s); location(s); savings and checking account numbers; authorized signatures; checkbook; statements; automatic bill payment; ATM cards, PINs, user names and passwords for online accounts		

Financial Assets: Sources of Income–Interest		
For each item: related documents, statements, certificates, lists, and the like	Physical location of these documents, statements, etc.	Contacts for additional information
❑ Safe deposit box(es)		
Bank name(s), address(es)		
Box number(s)		
Location of key(s) or combination(s) of lock(s)		
Authorized access names recognized by the bank(s)		

5 Financial Assets & Liabilities

Financial Assets: Retirement Accounts		
For each item: related documents, statements, certificates, lists, and the like	Physical location of these documents, statements, etc.	Contacts for additional information
❑ Annuity; charitable gift annuity		
❑ IRA		
❑ SIMPLE IRA		

Financial Assets: Retirement Accounts		
For each item: related documents, statements, certificates, lists, and the like	Physical location of these documents, statements, etc.	Contacts for additional information
❑ Roth IRA		
❑ SEP-IRA		
❑ Keogh		

5 Financial Assets & Liabilities

Financial Assets: Retirement Accounts		
For each item: related documents, statements, certificates, lists, and the like	Physical location of these documents, statements, etc.	Contacts for additional information
❑ 401K		
❑ 403B		
❑ Other retirement accounts		

Financial Assets: Investments		
For each item: related documents, statements, certificates, lists, and the like	Physical location of these documents, statements, etc.	Contacts for additional information
❑ Stocks		
❑ Mutual funds		
❑ Partnerships		
❑ U.S. Treasuries		

5 Financial Assets & Liabilities

Financial Assets: Investments		
For each item: related documents, statements, certificates, lists, and the like	Physical location of these documents, statements, etc.	Contacts for additional information
❑ U.S. bonds		
❑ State, municipal bonds		
❑ Corporate bonds		
❑ Certificates of Deposit (CDs)		

Financial Assets: Investments		
For each item: related documents, statements, certificates, lists, and the like	Physical location of these documents, statements, etc.	Contacts for additional information
❑ Money market funds		
❑ Commodities		
❑ Negotiable certificates		
❑ Foreign: currency, property, other assets		

5 Financial Assets & Liabilities

Financial Assets: Real Estate/Properties		
For each item: related documents, statements, certificates, lists, and the like	Physical location of these documents, statements, etc.	Contacts for additional information
❑ Primary residence (including joint ownership)		
❑ Other homes/timeshares (including joint ownership)		
❑ Commercial/rental/sublet properties; current tenants; contracts		

Financial Assets: Tangible Assets		
For each item: related documents, statements, certificates, lists, and the like	Physical location of these documents, statements, etc.	Contacts for additional information
For the following, provide make, model, year, ID #, ownership, title, registration #, financed or leased. ❑ Vehicles: auto, recreational (RV), off-road (ATV), snowmobile, motorcycle, truck, farm/heavy equipment; garage, storage location; service/maintenance records		
❑ Watercraft; marina, boat yard, storage location; service/maintenance records		

5 Financial Assets & Liabilities

Financial Assets: Tangible Assets		
For each item: related documents, statements, certificates, lists, and the like	Physical location of these documents, statements, etc.	Contacts for additional information
❑ Aircraft; airport, storage location; service/ maintenance records		
❑ Precious metals: gold, silver, other		
❑ Jewelry; appraisal records		

Financial Assets: Tangible Assets		
For each item: related documents, statements, certificates, lists, and the like	Physical location of these documents, statements, etc.	Contacts for additional information
❑ Investment grade coins, stamps; appraisal records		
❑ Antiques; appraisal records		
❑ Fine art; appraisal records		
❑ Valuable collections; appraisal records		

5 Financial Assets & Liabilities

Financial Assets: Other Assets		
For each item: related documents, statements, certificates, lists, and the like	Physical location of these documents, statements, etc.	Contacts for additional information
❑ Insurance policies with cash value		
❑ Anticipated inheritance and/or gifts: money, property, tangible assets		
❑ Lines of credit		

Financial Assets: Other Assets		
For each item: related documents, statements, certificates, lists, and the like	Physical location of these documents, statements, etc.	Contacts for additional information
For all credit, debit, travel cards: name, issuing company, number, expiration date; include where security codes, PINs can be found ❑ Credit cards, including banks, retailers/merchants, energy companies (such as Visa®, Macy's®, Exxon Mobil®)		

5 Financial Assets & Liabilities

Financial Assets: Other Assets		
For each item: related documents, statements, certificates, lists, and the like	Physical location of these documents, statements, etc.	Contacts for additional information
❑ Debit cards		
❑ Travel cards with awards: airlines, rental cars, hotels		
❑ Uncollected legal judgments, claims, and pending lawsuits in my favor; additional money owed to me		

Financial Liabilities: Loans/Promissory Notes Due		
For each item: related documents, statements, certificates, lists, and the like	Physical location of these documents, statements, etc.	Contacts for additional information
❑ Mortgages/reverse mortgages: residences		
❑ Mortgages/reverse mortgages: commercial/rental properties		
❑ Home equity loans		

5 Financial Assets & Liabilities

Financial Liabilities: Loans/Promissory Notes Due		
For each item: related documents, statements, certificates, lists, and the like	Physical location of these documents, statements, etc.	Contacts for additional information
❑ Vehicles, watercraft, aircraft loan/lease		
❑ Personal loans/family loans (including arrangements); guarantor of loans		
❑ Margin loans		

Financial Liabilities: Obligations		
For each item: related documents, statements, certificates, lists, and the like	Physical location of these documents, statements, etc.	Contacts for additional information
❑ Alimony/child support		
❑ Credit card debt (including banks, retail/merchants, energy companies)		
❑ Property rental/lease obligations; condo fees, assessments		
❑ Automatic deductions from bank accounts (for recurring bill payments, monthly fees, insurance premiums, and the like)		

5 Financial Assets & Liabilities

Financial Liabilities: Obligations		
For each item: related documents, statements, certificates, lists, and the like	Physical location of these documents, statements, etc.	Contacts for additional information
❑ Promised contributions to organizations; pledges, bequests, endowments		
❑ Written or verbal agreements to provide financial support or care for others: children, adults		
❑ Unpaid legal judgments, claims, pending lawsuits not in my favor; money owed to others		
❑ Access to accounts, documents, files on home computer/websites; account names and numbers, PINs, screen names, user names, passwords		

Private Business Ownership

This chapter is the place to record information about your ownership in a private business. If you own, or have part ownership in, a private business—for profit or not-for-profit—you will want to provide essential information about this enterprise for your family, friends, and advisers. As this chapter deals only with the basic information associated with a business, be sure to add anything else you believe should be known.

This chapter addresses the following items.

Organizational Information 73

- Business name, type of business, date of formation
- Business locations, addresses, phone numbers
- Business website
- Form of ownership
- Percentage interest of ownership I hold
- Other partners; percentage interest of ownership they hold
- Board of Directors
- Other organizational papers
- Verbal agreements among partners
- Plans for the continuation of the business
- Essential employees; employment contracts
- Employment records
- Organization's attorney, accountant

Financial Information 77

- Major assets
- Major liabilities
- Patents, copyrights, trademarks, royalties
- Major customers/clients
- Key vendors, suppliers
- Key contracts
- Financial records
- Insurance policies
- Benefit plans

In This Chapter

In the **first column** of the following tables, check off each pertinent item and record the title of documents, statements, records, or the like that contain the related information. (See the sample table on page 72.) If some documents do not exist, you may create and reference them, or you may enter your response to an item directly in the appropriate space.

In the **second column**, enter the physical location of these documents. In the **third column**, enter the contact information for those who can provide additional information about the business; include their names, addresses, phone numbers, and email addresses.

6 Private Business Ownership

Sample Table

Organizational Information		
For each item: related documents, statements, certificates, lists, and the like	**Physical location of these documents, statements, etc.**	**Contacts for additional information**
☑ **Business name; type of business; date of formation** • Essential Consulting, Inc. • Management consulting • January 1, 2001	The original papers are in my attorney's safe; copies are in my file cabinet at home.	Attorney: H.I. Jones 123 Any Street City, State 12345 555-121-1212 hijones@- - - -.com
☑ **Business locations, addresses, phone numbers** **Main location:** 123 Any Street City, State 12345 **Main phone number:** 555-121-1212	Locations and phone numbers of other company sites can be found on the business web site.	
☑ **Business website** www.- - - -.com	Additional information about the website is in my file cabinet at home.	See above
☑ **Form of ownership** Limited Liability Company	See above	See above

Organizational Information		
For each item: related documents, statements, certificates, lists, and the like	Physical location of these documents, statements, etc.	Contacts for additional information
❑ Business name; type of business; date of formation		
❑ Business locations, addresses, phone numbers		
❑ Business website		
❑ Form of ownership		

6 Private Business Ownership

Organizational Information		
For each item: related documents, statements, certificates, lists, and the like	Physical location of these documents, etc.	Contacts for additional information
❑ Percentage interest of ownership I hold		
❑ Other partners; percentage interest of ownership they hold		
❑ Board of Directors		
❑ Other organizational papers, including articles of incorporation, plans for succession		

Organizational Information		
For each item: related documents, statements, certificates, lists, and the like	Physical location of these documents, statements, etc.	Contacts for additional information
❑ Verbal agreements among partners, such as right of first refusal		
❑ Plans for the continuation of the business		
❑ Essential employees		

6 Private Business Ownership

Organizational Information		
For each item: related documents, statements, certificates, lists, and the like	Physical location of these documents, statements, etc.	Contacts for additional information
❑ Employment contracts		
❑ Employment records		
❑ Attorney, accountant		

Financial Information		
For each item: related documents, statements, certificates, lists, and the like	Physical location of these documents, statements, etc.	Contacts for additional information
❑ Major assets		
❑ Major liabilities		
❑ Patents, copyrights, trademarks, royalties		

6 Private Business Ownership

Financial Information		
For each item: related documents, statements, certificates, lists, and the like	Physical location of these documents, statements, etc.	Contacts for additional information
❑ Major customers/clients		
❑ Key vendors, suppliers		
❑ Key contracts		

Financial Information		
For each item: related documents, statements, certificates, lists, and the like	Physical location of these documents, statements, etc.	Contacts for additional information
❑ Financial records; tax numbers		
❑ Insurance policies		
❑ Benefit plans		

6 Private Business Ownership

Notes

Additional Important Documents

This chapter is the place to record pertinent information about a variety of additional documents. These documents, while not estate records, will be important to your family, friends, and advisers who will need easy access to them if you become disabled and when you die. This is especially true for the executor of your estate and the person(s) who holds your durable power of attorney. Note: be careful not to place anything in your safe deposit box that might be needed in an emergency unless someone has been given joint access to it. This chapter deals with the following documents, statements, certificates, lists, and the like.

Insurance Related 83
- Social Security card and statements
- Medicare Plan, Medicare Supplemental Insurance (Medigap), dental, other health care insurance cards

Family 84
- Marriage, birth, death certificates
- Change of legal name, supporting documents

Citizenship 85
- Passport(s)
- Citizenship/naturalization papers
- U.S. visa, green card

Ownership 86
- Primary, other residences: deed, record of purchase, and the like
- Vehicles, watercraft, aircraft: title, records of purchase/lease, and the like

Financial 91
- Tax records and backup files
- Current financial records

Other 93
- Professional licenses to practice
- Military service papers
- Personal calendar, schedule
- Access to accounts, documents, files

In This Chapter

In the **first column** of the following tables, check off all the items that apply to you and record the titles of related documents, statements, certificates, lists, and the like. Include any identification information such as certificate numbers. (See the sample table on page 82.) You also may choose to create and reference a new document or enter pertinent information directly in the space provided.

In the second column, enter where each document, statement, certificate, list, and the like is physically located. In the **third column**, list the people or organizations to contact for additional information; include their addresses, phone numbers, and email addresses.

7 Additional Important Documents

Sample Table

Insurance Related		
For each item: related documents, statements, certificates, lists, and the like	**Physical location of these documents, statements, etc.**	**Contacts for additional information**
☑ **Social Security card and statements** Social Security card Social Security statements - Benefit Amount - Benefit Statement SSA-1099	The original card is in my safe deposit box at my bank. With tax records in my file cabinet at home	Attorney: H.I. Jones 123 Any Street City, State 12345 555-121-1212 hijones@- - - -.com
☑ **Medicare Plan, Medicare Supplemental Insurance (Medigap), dental, other health care insurance cards** Medicare card Commonwealth Health Plan card	Both cards are in my wallet.	

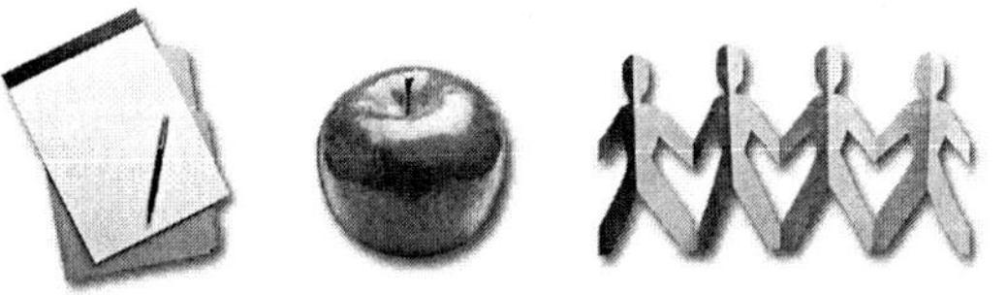

Insurance Related		
For each item: related documents, statements, certificates, lists, and the like	Physical location of these documents, statements, etc.	Contacts for additional information
❑ Social Security card and statements		
❑ Medicare Plan, Medicare Supplemental Insurance (Medigap), dental, other health care insurance cards		

7 Additional Important Documents

Family		
For each item: related documents, statements, certificates, lists, and the like	Physical location of these documents, statements, etc.	Contacts for additional information
❑ Marriage, birth, death certificates		
❑ Change of legal name, supporting documents		

Citizenship		
For each item: related documents, statements, certificates, lists, and the like	Physical location of these documents, statements, etc.	Contacts for additional information
❑ Passport(s)		
❑ Citizenship/naturalization papers		
❑ U.S. visa, green card		

7 Additional Important Documents

Ownership–Primary Residence		
For each item: related documents, statements, certificates, lists, and the like	Physical location of these documents, statements, etc.	Contacts for additional information
❑ Deed; mortgage; joint ownership		
❑ Record of purchase, capital improvements		
❑ Blueprints; site plan, well/septic system plans		
❑ Easements (utilities, passage)		

Ownership–Primary Residence		
For each item: related documents, statements, certificates, lists, and the like	Physical location of these documents, statements, etc.	Contacts for additional information
❑ Zoning, conservation, planning permits		
❑ Records of inspections (such as a septic system)		
❑ Condominium Master Deed, By-Laws, Rules; management company; fees, assessments		

7 Additional Important Documents

Ownership–Other Residence(s)		
For each item: related documents, statements, certificates, lists, and the like	Physical location of these documents, statements, etc.	Contacts for additional information
❑ Deed; mortgage for other residence(s); joint ownership		
❑ Record of purchase, capital improvements		
❑ Blueprints; site plan; well, septic system plans		
❑ Easements (utilities, passage)		

Ownership–Other Residence(s)		
For each item: related documents, statements, certificates, lists, and the like	Physical location of these documents, statements, etc.	Contacts for additional information
❑ Zoning, conservation, planning permits		
❑ Records of inspections (such as a septic system)		
❑ Condominium Master Deed, By-Laws, Rules; management company; fees, assessments		

7 Additional Important Documents

Ownership		
For each item: related documents, statements, certificates, lists, and the like	Physical location of these documents, statements, etc.	Contacts for additional information
Title, record of purchase/lease, registration, license to operate for the following three types of transportation: ❑ Vehicles: auto, recreational (RV), off-road (ATV), snowmobile, motorcycle, truck, farm/heavy equipment		
❑ Watercraft		
❑ Aircraft		

Financial		
For each item: related documents, statements, certificates, lists, and the like	Physical location of these documents, statements, etc.	Contacts for additional information
Tax records and backup files (such as receipts for medical, charitable deductions), current and past years for the following: ❑ Income tax: federal, state, local		
❑ Real estate tax		
❑ Sales tax		

7 Additional Important Documents

Financial		
For each item: related documents, statements, certificates, lists, and the like	Physical location of these documents, statements, etc.	Contacts for additional information
❑ Excise tax		
❑ Professionals who helped prepare tax returns		
❑ Current financial records: bills, records of bills paid, bank statements, check book, and the like		

Other		
For each item: related documents, statements, certificates, lists, and the like	Physical location of these documents, statements, etc.	Contacts for additional information
❑ Professional licenses to practice		
❑ Military service papers: branch, service/serial number, dates of service, discharge papers, pension, VA benefits		
❑ Personal calendar, schedule		
❑ Access to accounts, documents, files on home computer/websites; account names and numbers, PINs, screen names, user names, passwords		

Notes

Practical Details of My Everyday Life

This chapter is the place to record information about the practical details of your everyday life. Most of us forget just how complex our daily lives are — the kinds of demands we respond to, the number of people we deal with, the various places we must be, the services we give and receive from others, the organizations we belong to, and the different technologies we use. Each member of a family has his or her own list of household tasks, some of which may not be known to others. Even spouses or partners who have lived together and have shared responsibilities may not be aware of all that the other knows or does. If you become severely incapacitated and when you die, your family and friends may find that they lack information about many of the things you did and took care of, including the people you called for assistance.

The following is a list of the practical details that may define one's everyday life — the demands, activities, and people dealt with on a regular basis. In the **first column** of the following tables, check off those items that apply to you and record related information, such as documents, statements, certificates, lists, and the like. (See the sample table on page 97.) You also may choose to create and reference a new list, such as the names of key service providers or favorite charities; or you may record pertinent information directly in the space provided.

In the **second column**, enter the physical location of these documents, statements, certificates, lists, and the like. In the **third column**, list the names, addresses, phone numbers, and email addresses of those who can be contacted for additional information. Provide as much information as you think your family or friends will need when you are not around to help.

This chapter includes the items shown on the following page.

Notes

8 Practical Details of My Everyday Life

Notes

Home 98
- Primary residence, location; contracts signed
- People who have keys/combinations/codes to my residence, security system, safe, post office box, car(s)
- My pets

Religious/Spiritual Affiliation 100
- Church, temple, mosque, or other spiritual group
- Clergy
- Lay positions held
- Personal services received

Personal Service Providers 101
- Day care and babysitters for children
- Meal preparation
- Driver
- Tutor
- Personal trainer

Home Service Providers 102
- Key service people; service contracts

Utility Providers 108
- Electricity, heating, water, sewage, phone, TV, Internet

Technology in the Home 110
- Instructions for the operation of equipment; warranties
- My home computer(s)

Memberships/Interests 117
- Memberships in organizations; favorite charities; where I volunteer
- Subscriptions

Property in My Home 121
- Distinctive valuables
- Firearms
- Inventory of personal property

Employment 122
- Full-time, part-time
- Employer, location
- Occupation, position
- Union affiliation

Sample Table

Home		
For each item: related documents, statements, certificates, lists, and the like	**Physical location of these documents, statements, etc.**	**Contacts for additional information**
☑ **Primary residence and location (house, apartment, condominium, co-operative, retirement community, nursing home, mobile home)** Pondview Condominium 123 Any Street City, State 12345 **Assigned parking space location** 101 A	See below.	Attorney: H.I. Jones 123 Any Street City, State 12345 555-121-1212 hijones@- - - -.com
☑ **Contracts signed and the names of the landlord, owners, administrators, condominium or co-operative association officers, condo management company, and such** – Condo Unit Deed – Master Deed, By-Laws, Rules & Regulations – Condo Association Board – Management Company: Best Management Co.	The Unit Deed is in my safe deposit box. Other documents are in a folder in my file cabinet at home.	President Pondview Condominium 123 Any Street City, State 12345 555-121-1212

8 Practical Details of My Everyday Life

Home		
For each item: related documents, statements, certificates, lists, and the like	Physical location of these documents, statements, etc.	Contacts for additional information
❑ Primary residence and location (house, apartment, condo, co-op, retirement community, nursing home, mobile home) Assigned parking space location		
❑ Private office located outside of home		
❑ Contracts signed and the names of the landlord, owners, administrators, condominium or co-operative association officers, condo management company, and such		

Home		
For each item: related documents, statements, certificates, lists, and the like	Physical location of these documents, statements, etc.	Contacts for additional information
❑ People who have keys/combinations/codes to my: Primary residence Security system Safe Post office box Car(s)		
❑ My pets: breed, age, name, feeding requirements, favorite toys, boarding kennel, veterinarian, medical problems		

8 Practical Details of My Everyday Life

Religious/Spiritual Affiliation		
For each item: related documents, statements, certificates, lists, and the like	Physical location of these documents, statements, etc.	Contacts for additional information
❑ Church, temple, mosque, or other spiritual group		
❑ Clergy		
❑ Lay positions held		
❑ Personal services received		

Personal Service Providers		
For each item: related documents, statements, certificates, lists, and the like	Physical location of these documents, statements, etc.	Contacts for additional information
❑ Day care and baby sitters for children		
❑ Meal preparation		
❑ Driver		
❑ Tutor		
❑ Personal trainer		

8 Practical Details of My Everyday Life

Home Service Providers–People/Contracts		
For each item: related documents, statements, certificates, lists, and the like	Physical location of these documents, statements, etc.	Contacts for additional information
❑ Computer and peripherals–setup, instruction, repair		
❑ Other electronic equipment–setup, instruction, repair: television, DVD, VHS, DVR, stereo, MP3, cell phone, smartphone, PDA, GPS		

Home Service Providers–People/Contracts		
For each item: related documents, statements, certificates, lists, and the like	Physical location of these documents, statements, etc.	Contacts for additional information
❑ Detection and alarm systems: smoke, fire, carbon monoxide; security system; connection to police/fire departments/security company		
❑ Fire extinguisher servicing		
❑ Appliance repair		
❑ Vehicles: auto, recreational (RV), off-road (ATV), snowmobile, motorcycle, truck, farm/heavy equipment; dealers, repair facilities		

8 Practical Details of My Everyday Life

Home Service Providers–People/Contracts		
For each item: related documents, statements, certificates, lists, and the like	Physical location of these documents, statements, etc.	Contacts for additional information
❑ Watercraft: dealers, repair facilities, boat yard, marina		
❑ Aircraft: dealers, repair facilities, airport		
❑ Contractor		
❑ Electrician		

Home Service Providers–People/Contracts		
For each item: related documents, statements, certificates, lists, and the like	Physical location of these documents, statements, etc.	Contacts for additional information
❑ Heating/ventilation/air conditioning/ductwork		
❑ Carpenter, roofer		
❑ Plumber		
❑ Painter		

8 Practical Details of My Everyday Life

Home Service Providers–People/Contracts		
For each item: related documents, statements, certificates, lists, and the like	Physical location of these documents, statements, etc.	Contacts for additional information
❑ Handyman		
❑ Cleaners: residence, windows, chimney, gutters		
❑ Pest control		
❑ Yard: landscape, sprinkler system, tree service, firewood		

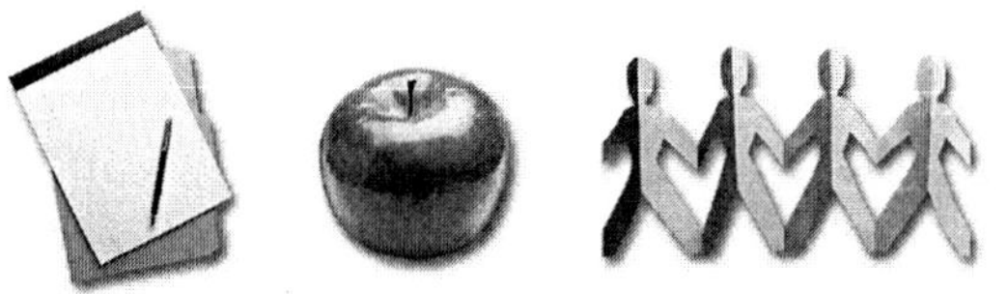

Home Service Providers–People/Contracts		
For each item: related documents, statements, certificates, lists, and the like	Physical location of these documents, statements, etc.	Contacts for additional information
❑ Pool/pond service		
❑ Snowplowing		
❑ Trash/garbage/recycling pickup		
❑ Septic system		

8 Practical Details of My Everyday Life

Utility Providers		
For each item: related documents, statements, certificates, lists, and the like	Physical location of these documents, statements, etc.	Contacts for additional information
❑ Electricity		
❑ Heating: natural gas, propane, heating oil, electricity		
❑ Water and sewage		

Utility Providers		
For each item: related documents, statements, certificates, lists, and the like	Physical location of these documents, statements, etc.	Contacts for additional information
❑ Phone services: landline, cell/mobile, Internet		
❑ TV: cable, fiber optic, satellite		
❑ Internet service provider, such as AOL, Yahoo, Google, Verizon, Comcast, RCN, Dish, Direct TV		

8 Practical Details of My Everyday Life

Technology In the Home–Instructions, Warranties		
For each item: related documents, statements, certificates, lists, and the like	Physical location of these documents, statements, etc.	Contacts for additional information
❑ Electrical panel; circuit breakers		
❑ Water and gas shutoff valves; sump pump		
❑ Detection and alarm systems: smoke, fire, carbon monoxide		

Technology In the Home–Instructions, Warranties		
For each item: related documents, statements, certificates, lists, and the like	Physical location of these documents, statements, etc.	Contacts for additional information
❑ Security system		
❑ Kitchen appliances		
❑ Washer and dryer		

8 Practical Details of My Everyday Life

Technology In the Home–Instructions, Warranties		
For each item: related documents, statements, certificates, lists, and the like	Physical location of these documents, statements, etc.	Contacts for additional information
❑ Heating and air conditioning		
❑ Television, DVD, VHS, DVR, stereo, MP3, cell phone, smartphone, PDA, GPS		
❑ Lighting; timers		

Technology In the Home–Instructions, Warranties		
For each item: related documents, statements, certificates, lists, and the like	Physical location of these documents, statements, etc.	Contacts for additional information
❑ Shop, studio equipment		
❑ Garage equipment		
❑ Yard and garden equipment, including sprinkler system		

8 Practical Details of My Everyday Life

Technology In the Home–Instructions, Warranties		
For each item: related documents, statements, certificates, lists, and the like	Physical location of these documents, statements, etc.	Contacts for additional information
❑ Swimming pool		
❑ Miscellaneous: equipment for photography, sports and recreation, hobbies, etc.		
❑ Emergency preparedness plans: fire, blizzard, hurricane, flood, earthquake, pandemic		

Technology In the Home–Computer(s)		
For each item: related documents, statements, certificates, lists, and the like	Physical location of these documents, statements, etc.	Contacts for additional information
❑ Type/make of computer(s), peripherals; operating system and version		
❑ Access to accounts, documents, files on home computer/websites; account names and numbers, PINs, screen names, user names, passwords		
❑ Applications software, ID numbers, product keys; CDs		

8 Practical Details of My Everyday Life

Technology In the Home–Computer(s)		
For each item: related documents, statements, certificates, lists, and the like	Physical location of these documents, statements, etc.	Contacts for additional information
❑ My own email address(es); contact list		
❑ Personal website: URL, host		
❑ Instruction manuals: computer(s), peripherals; operating system and applications software		
❑ Extra cables and equipment		

Memberships/Interests–Organizations		
For each item: related documents, statements, certificates, lists, and the like	Physical location of these documents, statements, etc.	Contacts for additional information
❑ Professional		
❑ Service/charitable		
❑ Fraternal		
❑ Civic/political/advocacy		
❑ Veterans		

8 Practical Details of My Everyday Life

Memberships/Interests–Organizations		
For each item: related documents, statements, certificates, lists, and the like	Physical location of these documents, statements, etc.	Contacts for additional information
❑ Social/cultural/ethnic		
❑ Religious		
❑ Educational		
❑ Arts, literary, book club		
❑ Self-help		

Memberships/Interests–Organizations		
For each item: related documents, statements, certificates, lists, and the like	Physical location of these documents, statements, etc.	Contacts for additional information
❑ Sports/recreational		
❑ Health club, gym, spa		
❑ Favorite charities		
❑ Where I volunteer		

8 Practical Details of My Everyday Life

Memberships/Interests–Subscriptions		
For each item: related documents, statements, certificates, lists, and the like	Physical location of these documents, statements, etc.	Contacts for additional information
❑ Magazines, journals		
❑ Newspapers		
❑ Newsletters		
❑ Online sites		

Property In My Home		
For each item: related documents, statements, certificates, lists, and the like	Physical location of these documents, statements, etc.	Contacts for additional information
❑ Distinctive valuables: jewelry, collections, types of items; storage areas; safe; security provided		
❑ Firearms, types; registration; storage area; security; child-proof measures		
❑ Inventory of personal property; supporting photos/videos		

8 Practical Details of My Everyday Life

Employment		
For each item: related documents, statements, certificates, lists, and the like	Physical location of these documents, statements, etc.	Contacts for additional information
❑ Full-time, part-time work		
❑ Self-employed; employed by others; location of work		
❑ Occupation, type of work, position		
❑ Union affiliation		

Significant People in My Life

This chapter is the place to record information about the significant people in your life and how they may be contacted. If you become disabled and when you die, your family, close friends, and advisers will need to contact a variety of people with whom you have been dealing. While there will be duplication of some names, such as physicians and attorneys, throughout *The Essential Organizer*, keep this information in each place for easy reference.

In the **first column** of the following tables, check off each item, the category of person or group, that is pertinent to you. (See the sample table on page 125.) Then record the titles of documents, statements, files, lists, and the like that contain names of these significant individuals and their contact information. You also may create and reference a new document, or you may enter the names directly in the space provided.

In the **second column**, record the physical location of any documents or devices containing these names. You may reference an existing list, files in your computer, entries in your Rolodex® file, and names in your cell phone, smartphone, or PDA directory. In the **third column**, enter the name of any person or organization who would have additional information about these people including addresses, phone numbers, and email addresses.

This chapter focuses on the categories of individuals and groups shown on the next page; add any others that you think are important.

Notes

9 Significant People in My Life

Notes

Family & Friends 126
- Immediate family members
- Extended family members
- Close friends

Personal Service Providers 127
- Caregivers
- Clergy and others
- Executor(s) of my estate
- Individual(s) with my power of attorney
- Individual(s) designated in my Health Care Proxy
- Trustees of my trust(s)
- Attorney
- Accountant
- Income tax preparer
- Financial planner/adviser
- Investment assets manager
- Stockbroker
- Insurance agents
- Veterinarian
- Realtor
- Travel agent

Health Care Providers 131
- Primary care physician, specialists, therapists, healer/practitioner
- Ophthalmologist, optometrist, optician
- Psychiatrist, therapist, counselor
- Dentists

Business & School Contacts 132
- Professional/business contacts
- Employer contacts
- Union contacts
- Contacts at the university, college, or other school attended or currently attending

Sample Table

Family & Friends		
For each item: related documents, statements, certificates, lists, and the like	**Physical location of these documents, statements, etc.**	**Contacts for additional information**
☑ **Immediate family members** Immediate family members are listed.	See Chapter 13 in this book, "My Immediate Family," for names and contact information for family members.	My husband will have additional information if needed.
☑ **Extended family members** These names are in my address book in my desk.	My desk drawer.	My husband will have additional information if needed.
☑ **Close friends** I have prepared a list of my close friends and their contact information.	This list is in a folder in my computer called "Close Friends," which is in my hard drive's "Documents" folder. Also printed and stored in my file cabinet at home.	My husband will have additional information if needed.

9 Significant People in My Life

Family & Friends		
For each item: related documents, statements, certificates, lists, and the like	Physical location of these documents, statements, etc.	Contacts for additional information
❑ Immediate family members		
❑ Extended family members		
❑ Close friends		

Professional Service Providers		
For each item: related documents, statements, certificates, lists, and the like	Physical location of these documents, statements, etc.	Contacts for additional information
❑ Caregivers, including family helpers such as a housekeeper, home health aide		
❑ Clergy and others at my church, temple, mosque, or other spiritual group		
❑ Executor(s) of my estate		
❑ Individual(s) with my power of attorney		

9 Significant People in My Life

Professional Service Providers		
For each item: related documents, statements, certificates, lists, and the like	Physical location of these documents, statements, etc.	Contacts for additional information
❑ Individual(s) designated in my Health Care Proxy		
❑ Trustees of my Trust(s)		
❑ Attorney		
❑ Accountant		

Professional Service Providers		
For each item: related documents, statements, certificates, lists, and the like	Physical location of these documents, statements, etc.	Contacts for additional information
❑ Income tax preparer		
❑ Financial planner/adviser		
❑ Investment assets manager		
❑ Stockbroker		

9 Significant People in My Life

Professional Service Providers		
For each item: related documents, statements, certificates, lists, and the like	Physical location of these documents, statements, etc.	Contacts for additional information
❑ Insurance agents		
❑ Veterinarian		
❑ Realtor		
❑ Travel agent		

Health Care Providers		
For each item: related documents, statements, certificates, lists, and the like	Physical location of these documents, statements, etc.	Contacts for additional information
❑ Primary care physician, specialists, physical and other therapists, healer/practitioner		
❑ Ophthalmologist, optometrist, optician		
❑ Psychiatrist, therapist, counselor		
❑ Dentists		

9 Significant People in My Life

Business & School Contacts		
For each item: related documents, statements, certificates, lists, and the like	Physical location of these documents, statements, etc.	Contacts for additional information
❑ Professional/business contacts		
❑ Employer contacts		
❑ Union contacts		
❑ Contacts at the university, college, or other school attended or currently attending		

Health Care & Wellness

This chapter provides the place to record information about a variety of items related to your health care and wellness. Whatever your age, if a time comes when family or friends must make decisions related to your health, they will need specific information about all aspects of your current medical, dental, and mental health care. In addition, they may need to know about any wellness activities you are involved in. The elements of health care are often very complex, and it may well be that no one person is aware of all the facets of your history and treatment. The information in this chapter of *The Essential Organizer* can help ensure that your medical care and related activities will be maintained at the level you desire.

In the **first column** of the following tables, check off each pertinent item and then record the names or titles of related documents, statements, certificates, lists, and the like. (See the sample table on page 135.) If such documents do not exist, you may create new ones and reference them, or you may enter pertinent information directly in the spaces provided. You also may want to collect important records from your doctors, dentists, medical labs, and hospitals and store them in one location for ease of access. Give special attention to any aspects of your family health history that might affect your care. In the **second column**, record where these documents are located. In the **third column**, note the people and organizations that can be contacted for additional information; include addresses, phone numbers, and email addresses. Many of these will be your health care providers.

Remember this is not the place to list confidential details of your medical condition, prognosis, or treatments. Rather you are asked to state where this information can be found in your home or at a medical facility.

This chapter addresses the following documents, records, and other information:

Notes

10 Health Care & Wellness

Notes

Medical Care 136
- Providers of medical care
- Medical conditions/treatment
- Financial records for services received

Short-Term Home Care Services ... 141
- Services used
- Providers of home care services
- Other temporary services used
- Financial records for services received

Dental Care 143
- Providers of dental care
- Existing chronic conditions
- Financial records for services received

Mental Health Care 145
- Providers of mental health care
- Mental health conditions/treatment
- Financial records for services received

Prescription Medications 147
- Current prescription medications
- Allergies to medications
- Pharmacies
- Pharmacists
- Prescription delivery

Family Health History 148
- Medical history
- Dental history
- Mental health history

Related Insurance 149
- Medical insurance
- Medicare Plan, Medicare Supplemental Insurance (Medigap)
- Dental insurance
- Long-term care insurance

Wellness Programs & Activities 150
- Participation in programs
- Dietary/nutritional plans
- Alternative therapies, medicines
- Spiritual activities

You may want to refer key people to your health care proxy and living will information, listed in Chapter 3, "Estate Planning Documents," and your insurance policies listed in Chapter 4, "Insurance Policies."

Sample Table

Medical Care–Providers		
For each item: related documents, statements, certificates, lists, and the like	**Physical location of these documents, statements, etc.**	**Contacts for additional information**
☑ **Organizations** Good Healthcare Associates – I have a copy of the enrollment contract.	The contract is in my file cabinet at home.	Good Healthcare Associates 123 Any Street City, State 12345 555-121-1212 gha@ - - - -.org
☑ **Doctors: primary care, specialists** The names of my primary care doctor and the specialists I use are all on a list I prepared.	This list is in my file cabinet at home.	
☑ **Nurse practitioners, other nurses** The name of the nurse practitioner I use is included on the above list.	See above	

10 Health Care & Wellness

Medical Care–Providers		
For each item: related documents, statements, certificates, lists, and the like	Physical location of these documents, statements, etc.	Contacts for additional information
❑ Organizations		
❑ Doctors: primary care, specialists		
❑ Nurse practitioners, other nurses		

Medical Care–Providers		
For each item: related documents, statements, certificates, lists, and the like	Physical location of these documents, statements, etc.	Contacts for additional information
❑ Therapists: physical, speech, other		
❑ Chiropractors		
❑ Healers, practitioners		

10 Health Care & Wellness

Medical Care–Conditions/Treatment		
For each item: related documents, statements, certificates, lists, and the like	Physical location of these documents, statements, etc.	Contacts for additional information
❑ Existing chronic conditions, allergies		
❑ Recurring exams; schedule		
❑ Tests and results, including blood pressure, cholesterol level, and the like		

Medical Care–Conditions/Treatment		
For each item: related documents, statements, certificates, lists, and the like	Physical location of these documents, statements, etc.	Contacts for additional information
❑ Current therapies, treatments		
❑ Regularly scheduled procedures, such as dialysis		
❑ Prescribed activities for rehabilitation and health maintenance		
❑ Medical equipment, garments, braces, supplies used; sources; how obtained		

10 Health Care & Wellness

Medical Care–Conditions/Treatment		
For each item: related documents, statements, certificates, lists, and the like	Physical location of these documents, statements, etc.	Contacts for additional information
❑ Medical records		
❑ Vision: eyeglass prescription; ophthalmologist, optometrist, optician		
❑ Hearing: hearing aid; audiologist		
❑ Financial records for services received		

Short-Term Home Care Services		
For each item: related documents, statements, certificates, lists, and the like	Physical location of these documents, statements, etc.	Contacts for additional information
❑ Services used (medical treatments, rehabilitation, nutrition, bathing-dressing-walking, palliative care)		
❑ Home care service organizations		
❑ Live-in caregivers		
❑ Visiting nurses, therapists, health aides, social workers		

Short-Term Home Care Services		
For each item: related documents, statements, certificates, lists, and the like	Physical location of these documents, statements, etc.	Contacts for additional information
❑ Medical equipment and supplies provided		
❑ Other temporary services used: housekeeping, cooking, driving		
❑ Financial records for services received		

Dental Care–Providers		
For each item: related documents, statements, certificates, lists, and the like	Physical location of these documents, statements, etc.	Contacts for additional information
❑ Organizations providing care		
❑ Dentists, specialists		
❑ Dental hygienist		
❑ Facilities used		

Dental Care–Conditions/Treatment		
For each item: related documents, statements, certificates, lists, and the like	Physical location of these documents, statements, etc.	Contacts for additional information
❑ Existing chronic conditions		
❑ Treatments; recurring exams; schedules		
❑ Dental records		
❑ Financial records for services received		

Mental Health Care–Providers		
For each item: related documents, statements, certificates, lists, and the like	Physical location of these documents, statements, etc.	Contacts for additional information
❑ Organizations providing care		
❑ Facilities used		
❑ Psychiatrists; therapists; counselors		

Mental Health Care–Conditions/Treatment		
For each item: related documents, statements, certificates, lists, and the like	Physical location of these documents, statements, etc.	Contacts for additional information
❑ Mental health conditions		
❑ Nature of treatment provided		
❑ Mental health records		
❑ Financial records for services received		

Prescription Medications		
For each item: related documents, statements, certificates, lists, and the like	Physical location of these documents, statements, etc.	Contacts for additional information
❑ Current prescription medications taken; prescribing physicians; other medicines used		
❑ Allergies to medications		
❑ Pharmacies: local, mail/phone/Internet order		
❑ Pharmacists		
❑ Prescription delivery: pickup, local delivery, mail		

10 Health Care & Wellness

Family Health History		
For each item: related documents, statements, certificates, lists, and the like	Physical location of these documents, statements, etc.	Contacts for additional information
❑ Medical history		
❑ Dental history		
❑ Mental health history		

Related Insurance		
For each item: related documents, statements, certificates, lists, and the like	Physical location of these documents, statements, etc.	Contacts for additional information
❑ Medical insurance		
❑ Medicare Plan, Medicare Supplemental Insurance (Medigap)		
❑ Dental insurance		
❑ Long-term care insurance		
❑ Critical illness insurance		

10 Health Care & Wellness

Wellness Programs & Activities		
For each item: related documents, statements, certificates, lists, and the like	Physical location of these documents, statements, etc.	Contacts for additional information
For all wellness programs and activities, include organizations (senior center, adult education center, YWCA/YMCA, local community, etc.) and facilities (fitness center, gym, pool, spa, etc.): ❑ Exercise, personal trainer, sports programs		
❑ Stress management programs		
❑ Weight loss programs		

Wellness Programs & Activities		
For each item: related documents, statements, certificates, lists, and the like	Physical location of these documents, statements, etc.	Contacts for additional information
❑ Smoking cessation programs		
❑ Dietary/nutritional plans		
❑ Alternative therapies, medicines		
❑ Spiritual activities		

Notes

Provisions if I Am Unable to Care for Myself

This chapter is the place to record information related to issues that will arise if you are incapacitated due to a critical illness or major disability. Regardless of your age, if you are unable to care for yourself, you may receive care in your home or you may be placed in an assisted living facility, a nursing home, or, in the most serious circumstance, a hospice. Given these possibilities, you probably will want to spell out your preferences for your treatment and for the care of your family and your home if no one will be living there. While no one enjoys anticipating serious illness or accidents and the consequences, it's wise to plan ahead by preparing documents that address the topics listed below. The information contained in this chapter is important for your family and others to have.

In the **first column** of the following tables, check off each pertinent item and record the titles of any documents, statements, certificates, lists, and the like that contain the names of individuals, instructions, or provisions. (See the sample table on page 155.) If relevant documents do not exist, you may create and reference them, or you may enter pertinent information directly in the spaces provided.

Then in the **second column**, record where these documents are located. In the **third column**, note the people who can be contacted for additional information; include their addresses, phone numbers, and email addresses.

This chapter includes the items shown on the next page.

Notes

11 Provisions if I Am Unable to Care for Myself

Notes

People to Inform 156

- People who must be notified immediately
- People who will care for my spouse, partner, or other family members
- People who have a copy of this book; those who should now be given a copy

People with Access 157

- Individuals who are authorized to have access to:
  - my home
  - my financial resources

Arrangements for My Care 158

- Preferred facility and arrangements
- Financial resources available, including long-term care plans and other insurance policies
- Items I want to take with me if I must leave home
- Contact I want with my church, temple, mosque, or other spiritual group

Home & Property 159

- Arrangements for the care of my pets
- Instructions for the protection and maintenance of my home
- Instructions for the care and disposition of my personal property
- Instructions for the payment of bills and continuation of contributions

In addition, you may want to direct key people to your health care proxy and living will, listed in Chapter 3, "Estate Planning Documents."

Sample Table

People to Inform		
For each item: related documents, statements, certificates, lists, and the like	**Physical location of these documents, statements, etc.**	**Contacts for additional information**
☑ **People who must be notified immediately** – My husband – My children – My close friend Barbara Malinsky – My pastor Rev. Charles Jefferson – My attorney H.I. Jones – My financial adviser Helen O'Neil	For contact information, see these chapters in this book: – 9 "Significant People in My Life" – 13 "My Immediate Family"	Attorney: H.I. Jones 123 Any Street City, State 12345 555-121-1212 hij@ - - - -.com My husband and attorney will know whom to contact.
☑ **People who will care for my spouse, partner, or other family members** – My husband and attorney have this information.	The document with this information is in my attorney's office and in my file cabinet.	Same as above
☑ **People who have a copy of this book** – My husband – My children – My close friend Barbara Malinsky – My attorney H.I. Jones	See also page v	Same as above

11 Provisions if I Am Unable to Care for Myself

People to Inform		
For each item: related documents, statements, certificates, lists, and the like	Physical location of these documents, statements, etc.	Contacts for additional information
❑ People who must be notified immediately		
❑ People who will care for my spouse, partner, or other family members		
❑ People who have a copy of this book		
❑ People who should now be given a copy		

People with Access		
For each item: related documents, statements, certificates, lists, and the like	Physical location of these documents, statements, etc.	Contacts for additional information
Family members, friends, and advisers who are authorized to have access to: ❑ Keys to the doors of my residence(s)		
❑ Alarm system code/key		
❑ Keys to my cars		
❑ Financial resources (those with my Power of Attorney; those listed on my joint accounts)		

11 Provisions if I Am Unable to Care for Myself

Arrangements for My Care		
For each item: related documents, statements, certificates, lists, and the like	Physical location of these documents, statements, etc.	Contacts for additional information
❑ Preferred facility and arrangements for home care, assisted living, nursing home, or hospice care		
❑ Financial resources available, including long-term care plans and insurance policies; benefits currently being received		
❑ Items I want to take with me if I must leave home		
❑ Contact I want with my church, temple, mosque, or other spiritual group		

Home & Property		
For each item: related documents, statements, certificates, lists, and the like	Physical location of these documents, statements, etc.	Contacts for additional information
❑ Arrangements for the care of my pets: breed, age, name, requirements for feeding, favorite toys, kennel used, veterinarian used, medical problems		
❑ Instructions for the protection and maintenance of my home until I return, it is sold, or ownership is otherwise transferred		
❑ Instructions for the care and disposition of my personal property if I will not be returning to my home		
❑ Instructions for the payment of bills and the continuation of contributions to organizations and gifts to individuals		

11 Provisions if I Am Unable to Care for Myself

Notes

Arrangements When I Die

This chapter is the place to record your wishes related to your funeral arrangements and to your home after you're gone. It isn't easy to think about your death and funeral, but it may be of some comfort to know that your family will understand your personal wishes. Moreover, they will feel less burdened if they do not have to guess about your preferences.

Space is also provided in this chapter to express your wishes for the care of your pets and the disposition of your home if you do not have a surviving spouse, partner, children, or others who will continue to live there. In addition, if you have not provided for the financial welfare of family helpers, such as a housekeeper or in-home health care provider, you may address that here. Finally, this is the place to include special information related to the settling of your estate, such as instructions to your executor, family members, and so on.

Identify the documents your family, friends, and advisers must be able to access immediately after you die, and be sure these will be readily available when needed. As a precaution, don't put your will, funeral instructions, and the like in your safe deposit box; in some circumstances, it cannot be opened without a court order.

In the **first column** of the following tables, check off each pertinent item and record the title of any documents, statements, certificates, lists, and the like that contain your instructions, preferences, and other relevant information. If such documents do not exist, you may wish to create and reference them, or you can enter the information directly in the spaces provided. (See the sample table on page 162.) In the **second column**, record where key documents are physically located. In the **third column**, identify the individuals who can be contacted for additional information; include their addresses, phone numbers, and email addresses.

This chapter includes the following:

People to Inform 163
- People and organizations that must be notified immediately
- People who will care for my spouse, partner, or other family members

Funeral Arrangements 163
- Funeral home, cemetery
- Disposition of remains
- Funeral/memorial service
- Death notice and obituary
- Administrative details

Home and Property 172
- Arrangements for my pets
- Protection and maintenance of my home
- Disposition of my possessions
- Provisions for family helpers
- Special instructions to my executor, family members, and others

12 Arrangements When I Die

Sample Table

People to Inform		
For each item: related documents, statements, certificates, lists, and the like	**Physical location of these documents, statements, etc.**	**Contacts for additional information**
☑ **People and organizations that must be notified immediately: family, close friends, clergy, advisers, business associates** There are many people to notify.	These individuals are listed in Chapter 9, "Significant People in My Life."	My wife and children will know whom to contact.
☑ **People who will care for my spouse, partner, or other family members** My wife and attorney have this information.	The document with this information is in my attorney's office and in my file cabinet.	Attorney: H.I. Jones 123 Any Street City, State 12345 555-121-1212 hij@ - - - -.com
Funeral Arrangements–Funeral Home & Cemetery		
☑ **Funeral home; preplanned arrangements; prepaid contract or other financial provisions** I have a contract for arrangements (not prepaid) with the S.G. Goldman Funeral Home 123 Any Street, City, State 12345	The contract is in a folder in my file cabinet at home.	Ms. Sandra Goldman 555-121-1212

People to Inform		
For each item: related documents, statements, certificates, lists, and the like	Physical location of these documents, statements, etc.	Contacts for additional information
❑ People and organizations that must be notified immediately: family, close friends, clergy, advisers, business associates		
❑ People who will care for my spouse, partner, or other family members		
Funeral Arrangements–Funeral Home & Cemetery		
❑ Funeral home; preplanned arrangements; prepaid contract or other financial provisions		
❑ Cemetery		

12 Arrangements When I Die

Funeral Arrangements–Funeral Home & Cemetery		
For each item: related documents, statements, certificates, lists, and the like	Physical location of these documents, statements, etc.	Contacts for additional information
❑ Burial lot/plot, mausoleum, columbarium; deed, supporting documents		
❑ Monument, headstone, plaque; personal or military marker; inscription/epitaph		
❑ Provisions for perpetual care		

Funeral Arrangements–Disposition of Remains		
For each item: related documents, statements, certificates, lists, and the like	Physical location of these documents, statements, etc.	Contacts for additional information
❑ If burial: in-ground or mausoleum entombment; preference for embalmment, casket, clothing, flag		
❑ If cremation: ashes buried, placed in a columbarium, kept in a home, or spread; preference for urn; if spread, the location		
❑ Authorization for the donation of my body for medical education, scientific study, or transplant		

12 Arrangements When I Die

Funeral Arrangements–Funeral/Memorial Service Preferences		
For each item: related documents, statements, certificates, lists, and the like	Physical location of these documents, statements, etc.	Contacts for additional information
❑ No service		
❑ Visitation/viewing/wake		
❑ Religious service: religious affiliation, clergy, ritual; timing; special customs		
❑ Non-religious service		
❑ Interment/graveside service		

Funeral Arrangements–Funeral/Memorial Service Preferences		
For each item: related documents, statements, certificates, lists, and the like	Physical location of these documents, statements, etc.	Contacts for additional information
❑ Military, other organization ceremony		
❑ Memorial service		
❑ Location: church, temple, mosque, other spiritual meeting place, funeral home, residence, other		
❑ Reception following the service		

12 Arrangements When I Die

Funeral Arrangements–Funeral/Memorial Service Preferences		
For each item: related documents, statements, certificates, lists, and the like	Physical location of these documents, statements, etc.	Contacts for additional information
❑ Public or private service		
❑ Open or closed casket		
❑ Time		
❑ Ritual to be followed		

Funeral Arrangements–Funeral/Memorial Service Preferences		
For each item: related documents, statements, certificates, lists, and the like	Physical location of these documents, statements, etc.	Contacts for additional information
❑ Officiated by whom		
❑ Speakers; eulogy		
❑ Readings		
❑ Music		
❑ Pallbearers		

12 Arrangements When I Die

Funeral Arrangements–Death Notice & Obituary		
For each item: related documents, statements, certificates, lists, and the like	Physical location of these documents, statements, etc.	Contacts for additional information
❑ Death notice contents		
❑ To be placed in these newspaper(s), publications		
❑ Obituary contents: what it should include; who should write it; existing material; photograph		
❑ To be placed in these newspaper(s), publications		

Funeral Arrangements–Administrative Details		
For each item: related documents, statements, certificates, lists, and the like	Physical location of these documents, statements, etc.	Contacts for additional information
❑ Means of settling funeral/memorial service and associated costs		
❑ Death certificates: distribution to these individuals		

12 Arrangements When I Die

Home & Property		
For each item: related documents, statements, certificates, lists, and the like	Physical location of these documents, statements, etc.	Contacts for additional information
❑ Arrangements for the care and placement of my pets if necessary: breed, age, name, feeding requirements, favorite toys, boarding kennel, veterinarian, medical problems		
❑ Protection and maintenance of my home until it is sold or ownership is otherwise transferred; continuation of insurance; preferred real estate agent		
❑ Arrangements for the disposition of my possessions not dealt with in my will or other documents.		

Home & Property		
For each item: related documents, statements, certificates, lists, and the like	Physical location of these documents, statements, etc.	Contacts for additional information
❑ Financial provisions for family helpers; legal documents containing these provisions		
❑ Special instructions to my executor, family members, attorney, and others regarding the settlement of my estate		

Notes

My Immediate Family

This chapter is the place to record basic information about you and your immediate family members, including names, contact information, date/place of birth, citizenship, and more. This information will help you and others in the future with legal issues, such as proof of legal residency. It will facilitate contact with family members who will want to know if you become seriously ill or pass away. It may be useful at a later time in settling your estate. It may contribute to the family history, and provide useful information when writing your obituary.

This chapter deals with the following categories of family members:

- Me
- My spouse or partner
- Other parent of my children
- My children or stepchildren
- My parents, stepparents, guardians, birth parents
- My brothers and/or sisters

Enter the family information on the blank lines provided on the following pages. If this information already exists in documents, record their titles and physical location. If such documents do not exist, you may create and reference these, or you may choose to enter your response to each query directly into the book. (Note: the family category being addressed is shown in the upper right hand corner of each page.)

There are no sample entries for this chapter.

Notes

13 My Immediate Family

Information About Me

1. Full legal name; nickname; maiden name; assumed names; any legal change of name:

2. Address of principal residence; other residences; mailing address(es), post office box:

3. Phone numbers (home, work, day, evening; cell/mobile; pager):

4. Email address(es):

5. Social networks:

6. Personal website URL:

7. Date and place of birth:

8. Social Security number:

9. Medicare/Medigap/dental/other health care insurance cards, numbers:

10. Driver's license (state and ID #):

11. Passport(s)–country, number, expiration date:

Information About Me

12. Country(ies) of citizenship:

13. Naturalization papers, long-term visa, or green card that establishes legal residency in the USA; title and identification numbers; location of documents:

14. Primary occupation; professional licenses:

15. Current/recent employer and address; last position; start and stop dates; contact information:

16. Union affiliation (International and Local); contact information:

17. College/university/other school attended or attending; major/program; degrees, dates; fraternity/sorority:

18. Military service–branch; dates of service; service/serial number:

13 My Immediate Family

My Spouse or Partner

1. Full legal name; nickname; maiden name; assumed names; any legal change of name:

2. Marital status before our marriage or union (single, divorced, annulled, widowed):

3. Location of divorce or annulment documents:

4. If deceased, date of death, location of death certificate; location of remains:

5. Address of principal residence and other current residences; mailing address(es), post office box:

6. Phone numbers (home, work, day, evening; cell/mobile; pager):

7. Email address(es):

8. Social networks:

9. Personal website URL:

10. Date and place of birth:

11. Social Security number:

12. Medicare/Medigap/dental/other health care insurance cards, numbers:

13. Driver's license (state and ID #):

14. Passport(s)–country, number, expiration date:

15. Country(ies) of citizenship:

16. Naturalization papers, long-term visa, or green card that establishes legal residency in the USA; title and identification numbers; location of documents:

17. Primary occupation; professional licenses:

18. Current/recent employer and address; last position; start and stop dates; contact information:

13 My Immediate Family

My Spouse or Partner

19. Union affiliation (International and Local); contact information:

20. College/university/other school attended or attending; major/program; degrees; dates; fraternity/sorority:

21. Military service–branch; dates of service; service/serial number:

Notes

The Other Parent of My Children
If not my current spouse or partner

1. Name of child/children:

2. Full legal name of other parent; nickname; maiden name; assumed names; any legal change of name:

3. Current marital status of other parent (single, married, civil union, divorced, annulled, widowed):

4. If deceased, date of death, location of death certificate; location of remains:

5. Addresses of principal residence, other current residences; mailing addresses, post office box:

6. Phone numbers (home, work, day, evening; cell/mobile; pager):

7. Email address(es):

8. Social networks:

9. Personal website URL:

10. Date and place of birth:

13 My Immediate Family

The Other Parent of My Children
If not my current spouse or partner

11. Social Security number:

12. Medicare/Medigap/dental/other health care insurance cards, numbers:

13. Driver's license (state and number):

14. Passport(s)–country, number, expiration date:

15. Country(ies) of citizenship:

16. Naturalization papers, long-term visa, or green card that establishes legal residency in the USA; title and identification numbers; location of documents:

17. Primary occupation; professional licenses:

18. Current employer and address; position; contact information:

The Other Parent of My Children
If not my current spouse or partner

19. Union affiliation (International and Local); contact information:

20. College/university/other school attended or attending; major/program; degrees; dates; fraternity/sorority:

21. Military service–branch; dates of service; service/serial number:

Notes

13 My Immediate Family

My Children or Stepchildren
This format is repeated four times.

1. Child's name:

2. Contact information, address of principal residence, post office box, phone numbers, email address(es):

3. Date and place of birth or adoption; location of birth certificate, adoption papers:

4. If deceased, date of death; location of death certificate; location of remains:

5. Social Security number:

6. Country(ies) of citizenship:

7. Passport(s)–country, number, expiration date:

8. Current employer and address; occupation/position; contact information:

9. Marital status; name of spouse or partner and contact information if living:

10. My grandchildren: names, dates and places of birth, Social Security numbers, contact information:

My Children or Stepchildren

1. Child's name:

2. Contact information, address of principal residence, post office box, phone numbers, email address(es):

3. Date and place of birth or adoption; location of birth certificate, adoption papers:

4. If deceased, date of death; location of death certificate; location of remains:

5. Social Security number:

6. Country(ies) of citizenship:

7. Passport(s)–country, number, expiration date:

8. Current employer and address; occupation/position; contact information:

9. Marital status; name of spouse or partner and contact information if living:

10. My grandchildren: names, dates and places of birth, Social Security numbers, contact information:

13 My Immediate Family

My Children or Stepchildren

1. Child's name:

2. Contact information, address of principal residence, post office box, phone numbers, email address(es):

3. Date and place of birth or adoption; location of birth certificate, adoption papers:

4. If deceased, date of death; location of death certificate; location of remains:

5. Social Security number:

6. Country(ies) of citizenship:

7. Passport(s)–country, number, expiration date:

8. Current employer and address; occupation/position; contact information:

9. Marital status; name of spouse or partner and contact information if living:

10. My grandchildren: names, dates and places of birth, Social Security numbers, contact information:

My Children or Stepchildren

1. Child's name:

2. Contact information, address of principal residence, post office box, phone numbers, email address(es):

3. Date and place of birth or adoption; location of birth certificate, adoption papers:

4. If deceased, date of death; location of death certificate; location of remains:

5. Social Security number:

6. Country(ies) of citizenship:

7. Passport(s)–country, number, expiration date:

8. Current employer and address; occupation/position; contact information:

9. Marital status; name of spouse or partner and contact information if living:

10. My grandchildren: names, dates and places of birth, Social Security numbers, contact information:

13 My Immediate Family

My Parents, Stepparents, Guardians, Birth Parents

1. Name of my father/stepfather/guardian/birth father:

2. If living, address of principal residence, post office box, phone numbers, email address(es):

3. If deceased, date of death, location of remains:

4. Country(ies) of citizenship:

5. Social Security number:

6. Name of my mother/stepmother/guardian/birth mother:

7. If living, address of principal residence, post office box, phone numbers, email address(es):

8. If deceased, date of death, location of remains:

9. Country(ies) of citizenship:

10. Social Security number:

11. I am adopted; location of supporting documents:

My Brothers & Sisters
This format is repeated four times.

1. Name: ______________________________

2. If living, address of principal residence, post office box, phone numbers, email address(es): ______________________________

____

____

____

3. If deceased, date of death, location of remains: ______________________________

____

4. Social Security number: ______________________________

5. Marital status; name of current spouse or partner; name of ex-spouse or partner; contact information: ______________________________

____

____

6. If current spouse or partner is deceased, date of death, location of remains: ______________________________

____

____

7. Names, addresses, contact information of their children (my nieces and nephews): ______________________________

____

____

____

____

____

____

____

13 My Immediate Family

My Brothers & Sisters

1. Name:

2. If living, address of principal residence, post office box, phone numbers, email address(es):

3. If deceased, date of death, location of remains:

4. Social Security number:

5. Marital status; name of current spouse or partner; name of ex-spouse or partner; contact information:

6. If current spouse or partner is deceased, date of death, location of remains:

7. Names, addresses, contact information of their children (my nieces and nephews):

My Brothers & Sisters

1. Name:

2. If living, address of principal residence, post office box, phone numbers, email address(es):

3. If deceased, date of death, location of remains:

4. Social Security number:

5. Marital status; name of current spouse or partner; name of ex-spouse or partner; contact information:

6. If current spouse or partner is deceased, date of death, location of remains:

7. Names, addresses, contact information of their children (my nieces and nephews):

13 My Immediate Family

My Brothers & Sisters

1. Name:

2. If living, address of principal residence, post office box, phone numbers, email address(es):

3. If deceased, date of death, location of remains:

4. Social Security number:

5. Marital status; name of current spouse or partner; name of ex-spouse or partner; contact information:

6. If current spouse or partner is deceased, date of death, location of remains:

7. Names, addresses, contact information of their children (my nieces and nephews):

Family History

This chapter is the place to record information related to your family's history. It can include information about people, places, events, dates, traditions, facts, and stories that you want to leave to the younger members of your family, especially to your children and grandchildren. Perhaps you'll be the first person in your family to compile this history. Much of this information may already exist in a written genealogy or family tree along with old photographs, letters, scrapbooks, newspaper clippings, and home movies/videos/audiotapes. If so, pull these together and tell others where they're located, for example, in your home or in digital form on the Internet. Consider adding your own personal history to the larger family chronicle.

You may have family artifacts or heirlooms—such as furniture, dishware, clothing, and tools—that you might want to document. Consider creating a book or computer file for recording information about each of these items, including a description of its origin, history, and significance to the family; include a photograph if possible.

Although it takes some time and effort, you might think about making an audio or video recording in which you talk about the family history, interview older family members, or comment on such items as photographs and artifacts. Perhaps other members of the family would like to help with this.

If you or your family have any significant medical and mental health history that later generations should know about, include it in the larger history. While this may be very sensitive information—and in fact may be unknown to some family members—its value to later generations can be significant. Be sure the information is accurate and can be verified. The U.S. Department of Health and Human Services provides a secure website with a useful form in which you can enter and save health information about yourself and other family members. Go to https:familyhistory.hhs.gov.

In This Chapter

In the **first column** of the following tables, record information about documents, statements, certificates, lists, recordings, and the like that relate to items associated with your family's history. (See the sample table on page 194.) You may also choose to create and reference a list of items or enter pertinent information directly in the space provided.

In the **second column**, state where these documents, recordings, and the like are physically located. In the **third column**, enter the names, addresses, phone numbers, and email addresses of those individuals who might be able to clarify or add to this history. They may have additional insights on family records, events, medical issues, and the like.

14 Family History

Sample Table

Family History: Documents & Recordings		
For each item: related documents, statements, certificates, lists, and the like	**Physical location of these documents, statements, etc.**	**Contacts for additional information**
☑ **Family documents, photographs, artifacts** A genealogy of my family has been written and distributed by my niece, Rachel LeBlanc. I also have old family photos and a scrapbook belonging to my great-grandmother. I have drawn up a list of the family antiques in my home, including quilts, a clock, a wash-stand, sleigh bells, and a table .	My copy is contained in a folder called, "Family History," in my file cabinet at home. A list of these items is in the above folder.	Rachel LeBlanc 123 Any Street City, State 12345 555-121-1212 rlb@- - - -.com Contact my wife.
☑ **Family recordings: movies, videotapes/DVDs, audiotapes/CDs** Rachel also has started holding video interviews with senior family members. I have transferred to a DVD a number of old home movies dating back to the 1930s. My children and grandchildren have a copy.	Rachel has these. See above	Contact Rachel. Contact my wife or my children.

Family History–Documents		
For each item: related documents, statements, certificates, lists, and the like	Physical location of these documents, statements, etc.	Contacts for additional information
❑ Family documents, photographs, artifacts		

14 Family History

Family History–Recordings		
For each item: related documents, statements, certificates, lists, and the like	Physical location of these documents, statements, etc.	Contacts for additional information
❑ Family recordings: movies, videotapes/DVDs, audiotapes/CDs		

Personal Communications to Family & Friends

This chapter is the place to record your plans for communicating private information to those family members, friends, and others who are important to you. Your message may include your personal thoughts, feelings, beliefs, values, experiences, life lessons, specific wishes, last words, and such.

You may choose to communicate this information in person, through a written letter or other document, by phone or email, or in an audio or video recording. Some of your thoughts may appropriately be provided in a group setting while others may be offered individually. Some communications may be carried out while you're alive; others can be delivered after you have died. Remember that an important benefit of talking with others face to face, especially with younger family members, is that they will have the chance to ask questions and express their thoughts and sentiments to you.

You may wish to consider writing an "ethical will" (www.ethicalwill.com). While this is not a legal document, it provides a formal way to share with others your values, beliefs, memories, and hopes for the future.

In the **first column** of the following tables, record the names of all documents or recordings you have prepared but have not passed on to others. (See the sample table on page 198.) In the **second column**, give the physical location of these documents or recordings. In the **third column**, list the individuals, such as your spouse, partner, or attorney, who have access to these documents or recordings and are responsible for distributing them to the persons you have designated after you die; include the former's addresses, phone numbers, and email addresses. To avoid misunderstandings, be sure to clearly specify for whom each communication is intended and when it is to be delivered.

An Option

When you have completed *The Essential Organizer*, consider getting together with select family members and friends to talk about your entries in the book. A discussion of these items, including the objectives of your estate planning, could include the personal thoughts you wish to pass on.

You may also wish to give special instructions (and perhaps a note of appreciation) to specific individuals, such as the caregiver of your spouse or partner, the appointed guardian or trustee for minor children or those with special needs, the executor of your estate, or the trustees of your trusts. These directives may be conveyed while you are living or after you're gone.

15 Personal Communications to Family & Friends

Sample Table

Personal Communications: Documents & Recordings		
For each item: related documents, statements, certificates, lists, and the like	**Physical location of these documents, statements, etc.**	**Contacts for additional information**
☑ **Personal documents** I have written an "ethical will" as a way of communicating to younger family members & close friends my key life experiences, what I have learned from these, & my values & beliefs. I intend to write special instructions for family caregivers and the executor of my estate.	The original is in my attorney's safe & a copy is in a folder in my file cabinet at home. My attorney will distribute this to family members & close friends when I die. I'll give these to my attorney who will see that they go to the appropriate individuals.	Attorney: H.I. Jones 123 Any Street City, State 12345 555-121-1212 hij@----.com
☑ **Personal recordings: videotapes/DVDs, audiotapes/CDs** My husband and I have videotaped a discussion of our life experiences including the highlights of our marriage and family through 2006. We have not yet decided when to distribute this to our children.	My attorney has a copy of this DVD in his safe. A copy is in my file cabinet at home.	See above

Personal Communications: Documents		
For each item: related documents, statements, certificates, lists, and the like	Physical location of these documents, statements, etc.	Contacts for additional information
❑ Personal documents		

15 Personal Communications to Family & Friends

Personal Communications: Recordings		
For each item: related documents, statements, certificates, lists, and the like	Physical location of these documents, statements, etc.	Contacts for additional information
❑ Personal recordings: videotapes/DVDs, audiotapes/CDs		

Saving & Storing Key Documents

This appendix presents information on how long key documents should be saved and the proper places to store them. If you have questions about these or other documents, consult your attorney or accountant. Different rules apply to different documents. Some records and papers should be saved indefinitely and others for lesser lengths of time.

Key Documents to Save Indefinitely

Estate Planning

- All standard estate planning documents, such as a will, durable power of attorney, trust agreement, and health care proxy

Financial

- Insurance policies: until expired or terminated
- Pension plan and retirement plan documents; contributions to retirement plans
- Documents related to passing on investments to heirs
- Loans that have been paid off
- Tax returns and audit reports (keep supporting documents for six years)
- Social Security, Medicare, other insurance cards

Business

- Documents related to the formation and operation of a private business
- Professional licenses to practice
- Copyrights and patents
- List of previous employers; memos related to job performance

Notes

Saving & Storing Key Documents

Notes

Family

- Birth and death certificates; baptismal, confirmation certificates, and the like
- Marriage certificate
- Agreements: prenuptial, divorce, legal separation, annulment, property settlement, child custody
- Adoption papers
- Change of legal name

Citizenship

- Citizenship/naturalization papers
- U.S. visa, green card that establishes legal residence

Home

- Documents related to the purchase of your home and other property, including deeds
- Receipts documenting capital improvements to your home and other property
- Documents related to the sale of your home and other property

Personal Property

- Receipts for major purchases (to establish date of purchase for warranties, to back up future insurance claims, to support resale of items, to document capital gains tax)
- Personal property inventory with supporting photographs or video

Other

- Military service and discharge papers
- Proof of education level–diplomas, transcripts, certificates

Documents to Save for Six Years

- Supporting documents for tax returns should be kept for six years if they are business related (for example, if you are self-employed); these include W-2s, 1099s, receipts for deductions, and cancelled checks or their images for tax payments; also, the IRS has six years to conduct an audit if it suspects income was under-reported by 25% or more.
- Records of investments purchased and sold (some suggest keeping these indefinitely)
- Annual summary investment statements from brokerage firms, asset management companies, banks, and the like
- Bank statements and cancelled checks or their images
- Annual summary statements for credit cards
- Social Security annual statements

Documents to Save for Other Lengths of Time

- Supporting documents for tax returns, such as W-2s, 1099s, receipts for deductions, cancelled checks or their images for tax payments should be kept for at least three years; the IRS has three years to conduct an audit.
- Monthly investment statements from brokerage firms, asset management companies, banks, and the like–keep until an annual summary statement is issued
- Monthly credit card statements–keep until an annual summary statement is issued
- Legal contracts and leases–keep for the life of the contract plus six years
- Documents related to the purchase/maintenance of vehicles, watercraft, aircraft, including titles–keep until sold
- Warranties–keep until they expire
- Personal medical records–keep until they are replaced with subsequent records
- Passport–keep until it expires and a new one is issued

Notes

Saving & Storing Key Documents

Notes

Where Key Documents Should Be Stored

There are several places where you will want to keep your key documents. The particular location will depend on the degree of security these documents require, the need for rapid access to them, and the ease of replacing them if lost.

Copies of certain documents, if lost, may be available from the originating source. For example, after you have died, your family should be able to get copies of your insurance policies from your insurance companies, securities records from your brokerage firm, and tax records from your accountant.

Safe Deposit Box

Records that are difficult to replace should be stored in your safe deposit box, the place of greatest security for most people. You may want to keep copies of these documents in your home for ease of reference.

- Negotiable certificates
- Property deeds
- Titles for vehicles, watercraft, aircraft
- Personal property inventory with supporting photographs or video
- Birth and death certificates
- Marriage certificate
- Agreements: prenuptial, divorce, legal separation, annulment, property settlement, child custody
- Change of legal name
- Citizenship/naturalization papers
- U.S. visa and green card that establish legal residence
- Passport(s)
- Military service and discharge papers

When you die, other people will not be permitted to remove items from your safe deposit box without court approval unless you have authorized joint access. Think carefully about where you store documents, such as your will, trust agreement, and funeral arrangements, that may be needed immediately by your attorney and estate executor.

Attorney's Safe

Original signed copies of key estate planning documents and other legal documents may be kept in your attorney's safe. These would be, for example, your will, durable power of attorney, declaration of homestead, trust agreements, health care proxy, living will, prenuptial agreement, and so on. If this is not possible, then these original documents should be stored in your safe deposit box, with the exceptions noted above.

Medical Facility

Some doctors will accept only original (not copies) advance medical directives, namely the health care proxy and living will. Check this out carefully and be sure the original documents are stored in the correct place.

Home Storage

Other records should be kept in a secure place in your home, such as a safe or fire-resistant file cabinet, that will protect them against water damage, fire, and theft. These records include such items as insurance policies, health care documents, and financial statements. This storage place should be known to family members and other trusted individuals and be easily accessible to them, especially if an emergency occurs; they must have access to the key or the combination to the lock.

Notes

Saving & Storing Key Documents

Notes

Guide to Finding Key Topics

A

Adoption papers, 32, 184-188, 202
Advance medical directives, 23-24, 26-27, 30

B

Birth certificate, 84, 184-187, 202, 204

C

Care of others documents, 31, 70, 173,
Cemetery. See Death, arrangements
Citizenship/naturalization papers, U.S. visa, green card, 85, 177, 179, 182, 202, 204

D

Death, arrangements
- funeral arrangements
  - administrative details, 171
  - cemetery, 163-164
  - death notice/obituary, 170
  - disposition of remains, 165
  - funeral home arrangements, 163
  - funeral/memorial service, 166-169
- home and property
  - financial provisions, 173
  - pets, 172
  - protection/maintenance, 172
  - special instructions, 173
- people to inform, 163

Death certificate, 84, 171, 178, 181, 184-187, 202, 204
Declaration of homestead, 26, 30, 205
Dental care, 143-144
Disability, arrangements, 153. See also Medical care, long-term care
Divorce, annulment, separation, child custody, property settlement, 24, 32, 178, 181, 202, 204
Durable power of attorney, 25, 29, 201, 205

E

Employment, 122
Essential Organizer Fast Track, The, 1
Estate executor, 9-10, 14, 18, 25, 29, 41, 81, 124, 127, 161, 173, 197, 205
Estate planning documents
- associated documents, 24, 32
- care of others, 24, 31
- definitions, 23, 25-27
- medical, 26, 30
- property and financial, 23, 25-26, 29-30, 32, 201, 205

Guide to Finding Key Topics

Estate financial analyses, plans, 23, 32
Ethical will, 197
Express Forms, The, 1

F

Family
  health history, 148
  history, 193-196
  information: self, spouse/partner, other parent of children, children/stepchildren, parents/stepparents/guardians/birth parents, brothers, sisters, 175-192
  personal communications, 197-200
Files, documents
  access on home computer/websites, 39, 70, 93, 115
  authorized persons, 154, 197, 205
  power of attorney, 25,29
  storage/security, 10, 13, 15, 18, 133, 204-205
Financial assets
  investments
    mutual funds, partnerships, stocks, U.S. treasuries, 57
    certificates of deposit, U.S./state/municipal/corporate bonds, 58
    commodities, foreign currency, money market funds, negotiable certificates, 59
  other assets
    credit/debit/travel cards, 65-66
    inheritance/gifts, insurance policies, lines of credit, 64
    claims, pending favorable lawsuits, uncollected legal judgments, 66
  real estate/properties
    commercial, rental, residences, timeshares, 60
    capital improvements, deeds, record of purchase, 88, 204
    other important documents, 86-89
  retirement accounts
    annuity, tax-advantaged, other, 54-56
  sources of income
    alimony/child support, annuity, distribution from trusts/gifts, royalties, stock options, 48
    deferred compensation, pension, profit sharing, salary, Social Security, veteran/government benefits, wages, workers' compensation, 46-47
    dividends from mutual funds, partnerships, stocks, 49
    interest (from)
      U.S. treasuries, U.S./state/municipal/corporate bonds, 50
      certificates of deposit, money market funds, personal loans to others, 51
      bank/credit union accounts, 52-53
  tangible assets
    antiques/fine art, coins/stamps, valuable collections, 63, 121, 202
    jewelry, precious metals, 62, 121, 202
    vehicles, watercraft, aircraft, 61-62, 202

Financial liabilities
  loans/promissory notes due
    family, margin, personal, vehicles, watercraft, aircraft, 68
    home equity, mortgages/reverse mortgages, 67
  obligations
    alimony/child support, credit card debt, property rental/lease obligations, automatic deductions from bank accounts, 69
    promised contributions to organizations, agreements to provide financial support, unpaid legal judgments/claims, 70, 159
Foundation, private, 26, 30
Funeral. See Death, arrangements

G

Guardian, 31, 188, 197

H

Health care. See Medical care
Health care proxy, 26-27, 30, 128, 134, 154, 201, 205
Home. See also Financial assets
  computer, 102, 115-116
  contractors, home service providers, 102-114
  disposition, sale (of home), 159,172
  electronics, 102, 112, 115-116
  emergency preparedness, 114
  equipment, facilities, instructions, maintenance, warranties, 102-114
  firearms, 122
  inventory of personal property, 122
  personal service providers, 101, 141-142
  primary residence, contracts, 60, 98, 159
  protection/maintenance, 99,159,172
  security, 99, 103, 111, 122,157
  utility providers, 108-109
  vehicles, 103-104
Home care services, short-term, 141-142

I

Insurance Policies
  business, 79
  disability, 35
  life, 36
  long-term care, 36, 149, 158
  medical/dental, 35, 83, 149
  Medicare Plan/Medicare Supplemental Insurance (Medigap), 35, 83, 134, 149, 176, 201
  other, 39
  property
    homeowner's, mortgage and title, personal liability, renter's, 37, 159, 172
    aircraft, vehicles, watercraft, 38
  travel, accidental death, 36
Investments. See Financial assets

Guide to Finding Key Topics

L

Legal issues, pending, 32
Licenses
  driver's, 90,176
  to practice, 177
Living will, 27, 30, 205
Loans/promissory notes due. See Financial liabilities
Long-term care. See Insurance

M

Marriage certificate, 84, 204
Medical care
  conditions, treatments, therapies, 138-139
  dental, 143-144
  documents, 140,142,144,146
  equipment, 139, 142
  family history, 148
  home care, 141-142
  insurance, 149. See Insurance
  long-term care
    arrangements, facilities, 158
    insurance. See Insurance
  mental health, 145-146
  prescription medications, pharmacy, 147
  providers, 136-137
  vision, hearing, 140
  wellness programs, activities, 150-151
Medicare plan, Medicare Supplemental Insurance (Medigap).
  See Insurance
Memberships, interests
  charities, organizations, 117-120, 150
  subscriptions, 120
Military service, 93, 167, 177, 204

O

Obligations, financial. See Financial liabilities

P

Passport, 85, 176, 203, 204
Private business ownership
  financial information
    assets, copyrights, liabilities, patents, royalties, trademarks, 77
    clients, contracts, customers, suppliers, vendors, 78
    benefit plans, financial records, insurance policies, 79
  organizational information
    business name, date of formation, type of business, 73
    addresses/phone numbers, form of ownership, locations, website, 73
    board of directors, other papers, partners' percentage interest of ownership, 74
    continuation plans, essential employees, verbal partner agreements, 75

accountant, attorney, employee contracts, employment
records, 76
Pets, 99, 159, 172
Physicians. See Medical care
Prenuptial agreement, 32, 204

R

Real estate/properties. See Financial assets
Religious/spiritual
clergy, church/temple/mosque/other spiritual group,
lay involvement, services received, 100, 158, 163-169
Residence(s). See Financial assets, Home
Retirement accounts. See Financial assets

S

Safe deposit box, 53, 81, 161, 204-205
Security. See Files, documents, Home
Service providers (personal)
day care/babysitters, driver, meal preparation, trainer, tutor, 101
Social Security
card, 83, 201
income, 46, 203
personal number, iv, 176
Sources of income. See Financial assets
Subscriptions. See Memberships

T

Tangible, other assets, See Financial assets
Tax records
excise, income, real estate, sales, 91, 203
current records, tax preparers, 92
Technology. See Home
The Essential Organizer
completeness, accessibility, 13
contents, 11
disclaimer, 15
distribution, v, 14-15, 156
getting started, 13
how to use, 17-18
purpose and benefits, 9
recording essential information, 12
updating, 15
worksheet instructions, 17-21
Trust agreement, 25-26, 29

W

Wellness programs, activities, 150-151
Will, 25, 29, 201, 25
Websites
business, 73
data storage, 18, 41
personal, 116, 176
resources, 12, 193, 197